View of Richmond, Va., [1853]. Lithograph after John William Hill. [Cat. No. 71]. Graphic Arts Collection. Gift of Leonard L. Milberg '53.

Pride of Place

Early American Views
from the Collection of
Leonard L. Milberg '53

BY DALE ROYLANCE AND
NANCY FINLAY

PRINCETON UNIVERSITY LIBRARY

1983

COLLECTOR'S PREFACE
By Leonard L. Milberg '53

My Princeton education undoubtedly had something to do with my becoming a collector of early nineteenth-century American views. However, I took no art courses at the University. I concentrated on European history and literature; and I believe that Eric Goldman's history class and a literature survey course were my only exposure to nineteenth-century America at that time.

I have posited to myself that, since I am a first-generation American, my art interest was stimulated by a desire to create my own native antecedents. More likely the United States Army bore responsibility for my collecting proclivities. While stationed in Alaska for two years, I discovered a book store in Anchorage with a large supply of art books. I began reading about the Impressionists, moved backwards to the Renaissance, and then forward to the Baroque. Fifteen years later, when I stumbled upon the marvelous I. N. Phelps Stokes Collection of American views at the New York Public Library, my quest had ended, and my journey of collecting had begun.

Perhaps if I had been wealthier, I might have bought paintings. But I could afford prints, and I loved them at first sight. I found that at times the ingenuousness of vision and the luminosity of execution of the printmakers evoked for me a mood of enchantment—the magic of time stood still. I felt as Frank Lloyd Wright did when he averred that he was "enslaved" by Japanese prints: "because it is no secret that the prints choose whom they love and there is no salvation but surrender."

I wish to compliment Nancy Finlay for her first-rate scholarship in researching and cataloging the prints and artists.

The Library's Rare Book Division is fortunate to have Richard M. Ludwig—an extraordinarily able, enthusiastic, and thoughtful man—as its head. The old saw that goes, "Ask a busy man if you need to get something done" must have been a reference to Dick.

The Old Print Shop, my principal dealer, is an unsung, singular institution that has kept alive the traditions of nineteenth-century American genre art and prints for three generations. They have supplied Presidents, museums, and ordinary folk. The shop's current proprietor, Mr. Kenneth Newman, is assisted by his son Robert. Mr. Newman is a gentleman whose integrity, courtesy, and knowledge have made my visits to Lexington Avenue a great joy.

It was a felicitous day for me when I met Dale Roylance. He was the first person I knew who fully shared my enthusiasm for American views. We explored the field together as kindred spirits. We agreed that aquatints were superb, and that William James Bennett and John William Hill were masters. Dale made me feel that my collection was important because it documented a forgotten America; and he helped me understand the various techniques of printmaking. I started a print collection at the Library because I knew Dale was there to care for it.

This exhibit is a glorious occasion for me. I thank the Princeton University Library for making it possible.

PLATE 1   View Near Hudson. No. 12 of the Hudson River Port Folio. Aquatint by John Hill after William Guy Wall. [Cat. No. 25].
Graphic Arts Collection. Gift of Leonard L. Milberg '53.

PRIDE OF PLACE
Early American Views from
the Collection of Leonard L. Milberg '53

And what shall the pictures be that I hang on the walls, . . .
Pictures of growing spring and farms and homes, . . .
In the distance the flowing glaze, the breast of the river,
   with a wind-dapple here and there,
With ranging hills on the banks, with many a line against
   the sky, and shadows,
And the city at hand with dwellings so dense, and stacks of
   chimneys,
And all the scenes of life and the workshops, and the
   workmen homeward returning.
     Walt Whitman, "When Lilacs Last in the Dooryard Bloom'd"

American landscape and topographical prints of the early nineteenth century reveal the printmakers' vision of America at that time as an unspoiled and natural, almost Arcadian, land. Such prints reveal expansive skies above deep pastoral vistas, broken only by church steeples of infant towns. Roads are more important as landscape composition than as transportation, and habitation is barely indicated by lone accents of a small solitary figure or a distant white sail. It is a beautiful, highly romantic vision of an America now almost lost except for a series of engraved prints issued as bound portfolios in the early decades of the nineteenth century. It was as if the artists and printmakers of these engraved views had premonitions of the fate of these quiet scenes and made the most determined efforts to preserve this early undisturbed American landscape in printed pictures for later generations.

The first of this series of portfolios depicting the early American landscape was the *Scenographia Americana*, issued in London in 1768. It includes several views of the Hudson River engraved by Paul Sandby (1725-1809), an artist well established in England as a painter of romantic landscape. The Hudson was to be a chief source of inspiration for both visiting European and American artists. The river's magnificent vistas were perfect as scenic subjects in the grand academic tradition of Claude Lorrain, and its calm waters made transportation as idyllic as the Rhine itself. Two watercolor artists from Great Britain, William Guy Wall (1792-c. 1864) and Joshua Shaw (c. 1777-1860) arrived in America to embark almost at once on the creation of watercolors of the scenes of the Hudson and its surrounding countryside. Shaw settled in Philadelphia in 1817, Wall in New York in 1818. By 1820, another English trained artist, John Hill (1770-1850), had engraved the plates and published in portfolio Shaw's *Picturesque Views of American Scenery* and Wall's *Hudson River Port Folio*. Wall's *Port Folio* soon proved both popular and influential and appeared in several editions between 1820 and 1828. Both Wall and Shaw imbued their American scenes with a lyrical romanticism first learned in England, but both artists recognized the great natural beauty of America. The introduction to *Picturesque Views* describes America as "unsung and undescribed" and declares proudly "Our country abounds with Scenery comprehending all varieties of the sublime, the beautiful and the picturesque in nature."

Despite the pastoral imagery of the Hill and Shaw portfolios, urbanization of the land was inevitable and already well on its way. Boston, Philadelphia, and New York already had century-old iconographies. Fanciful views of these American cities became common in Europe during the eighteenth century in a type of popular print known as *vue d'optique* perspectives. A special tabletop apparatus of a mounted lens placed at an angle to a mirror reflected these curious prints to create effects of three dimensions. The fashionableness of this optical device, first in Europe and then in America, may be observed in the frequent placement of *vue d'optique* viewers in eighteenth-century interiors, including the parlor of Jefferson's Monticello and the Bainbridge House in Princeton. *Vue d'optique* prints are always recognizable by their reversed, mirror image title and primitive coloring. Several of these naive views of American cities, labeled in mirror-image lettering NEW YORCK, BOSTON or PHILADELPHIA, bear little resemblance to any actual American town, but helped to establish a strong popular tradition for the engraved city view in America.

More accurate city views first appeared in the earliest American periodicals. Paul Revere and Samuel Hill engraved primitive but honestly observed architectural images of eighteenth-century Boston for the *American Magazine* and the *Massachusetts Magazine*. These small octavo images are dwarfed, however, by a series of spectacular folio-size engravings created early in the eighteenth century of Boston, New York, Philadelphia, and Charleston. These extravagantly large views, consisting of four folio engravings pieced together to form a panoramic strip, proudly display America's most flourishing harbors, replete with ships with unfurled sails, their pennants flying and their cannons puffing away in artillery salutes. City pride has strong proclamation in these first major American city prints, which announce to the world that America now has its own cities, cities that would soon challenge the importance of any of the older cities of Europe.

Philadelphia, as America's capital from 1790-1800, has the distinction of not only a rich eighteenth-century iconography, but its own highly distinguished resident topographer. William Birch (1775-1834) drew, engraved (with his son Thomas Birch) and published *The City of Philadelphia* in Philadelphia in the year 1800. It was the first important series of American city views created entirely in America. Birch's careful documentations of Philadelphia's Georgian streetscapes are not only

meticulous in their accuracy of perspective and detail, but have a stylistic grace of their own that bespeaks a sophisticated, worldly city. It is a new American metropolis, far removed from the romantic wildness of the *Hudson River Port Folio*.

New York City was also showing signs of becoming a vigorous new world metropolis, and during the early nineteenth century attracted several genteel foreign visitors, all with considerable gifts for painting in watercolor. Diary-sketchbooks and watercolors recording their travels in America were created by the Russian Pavel Petrovich Svinin, the French Baroness Hyde de Neuville, the Italian Nicolino Calyo, and the Swedish nobleman, Axel Klinckowström. Klinckowström, in his visit to New York, painted a particularly elegant view of City Hall and Broadway of the early nineteenth century, but omitted showing in the painting at least one lingering rustic detail recorded in the engraving and text of his book on the United States in 1824: ". . . pigs are allowed to run loose on the streets. These pigs have on several occasions been the cause of remarkable scenes, jumping about and bowling over richly dressed ladies."

It was, however, English visitors to America who did the most to influence the direction of American landscape art. An early tradition of topographical watercolor painting was established in America by the immigration of the English artists already described, including William Birch in 1794, John Hill in 1816, Joshua Shaw in 1817 and William Guy Wall in 1818. The availability of watercolor supplies also encouraged American development of the art at this time. "Osborne's Superfine American Water Colors, equal to any imported," were first advertised in Philadelphia in 1824. Early American drawing books also favored watercolor. Archibald Robertson's *Elements of the Graphic Arts* (New York: 1802), and Fielding Lucas's

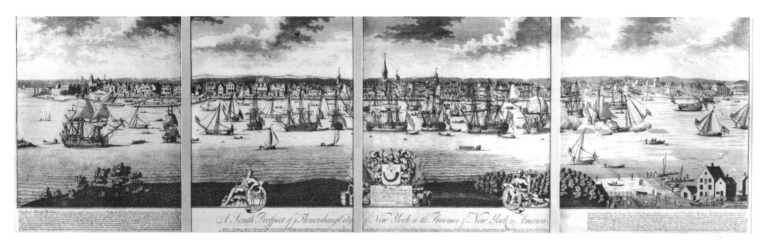

PLATE 2   A South Prospect of Ye Flourishing City of New York, 1746. Line engraving after William Burgis. I. N. Phelps Stokes Collection, The New York Public Library, Astor, Lenox and Tilden Foundation.

The Art of Coloring and Painting Landscapes (Baltimore: 1815) were the first to introduce American scenery as appropriate subject.

George Harvey (c. 1800-1878) first visited America from England in 1820. By 1833, he settled in Hastings-on-Hudson. Harvey first painted in the academic style of William Guy Wall, but developed a far more personal style concerned with effects of atmosphere, light and color. A group of forty watercolors he called "Atmospherics" were intended for a book, *Harvey's Atmospheric Scenery*, but only four, representing the seasons, were reproduced, engraved by William James Bennett, in *Harvey's Scenes of the Primitive Forest* (New York: 1841).

Another English artist, William Henry Bartlett (1809-1854), created his own American Grand Tour in one of the most popular of all books of illustrated American travel, *American Scenery* (London: 1840). Bartlett was a highly skilled watercolor painter and his fluid drawings present a far different scene from the tightly compressed steel engravings used to reproduce his American views.

The great number of these early watercolors of American scenery are a reminder of the great popularity of the technique of watercolor drawings in Europe and most particularly in England at this time. The unusual prevalence of watercolor also greatly stimulated the development of an important eighteenth- and nineteenth-century printmaking process, aquatint. This intaglio technique, in which flat tonalities are created on the copper printing plate by etching the plate through sprinkled resin dust, imitated to perfection the same tonal effects as watercolor. One of the greatest of all color plate books in the history of art and science, John James Audubon's *Birds of America*, is superbly printed in aquatint. Its engraver, Robert Havell, Jr., emigrated to America early in the nineteenth century to further record the American scene in several important city views. Another equally remarkable aquatint engraver, William James Bennett (1787-1844), arrived in America from England in 1816, and quickly became active as an engraver. Travelling to the important American cities of the day, including Boston, Baltimore, Washington, and Richmond, Bennett created in a series of aquatint engravings the classic nineteenth-century view of each of these cities. All have a quality of happy inspiration that denies all suggestion of any city discomforts of poverty, dirt, congestion or turmoil. Serenity reigns supreme with mirror-smooth harbors, decoratively becalmed sailing ships, and sunlit city horizons. Any storms will quickly pass in these halcyon visions. Could this gently wind-tossed English harbor scene really be Staten Island, this American Athens Baltimore, this marble Acropolis Richmond, or this Virgilian prospect Detroit? Perhaps. In the first half of the nineteenth century these cities were still young and full of the ardent optimism of a new Republic. As prints, Bennett's aquatints are equal in finish and elegance of style to the finest of English colored aquatints.

The watercolors of Harvey, Bartlett, and Bennett, and the aquatint prints made from them, helped to establish the legitimacy of watercolor painting as a fine art in America, and by 1850, a number of artists formed the New York Water Color Society. One of its earliest members was John William Hill (1812-1879). Hill was the son of John Hill, the engraver of Wall's *Hudson River Port Folio* and Shaw's *Picturesque Views*. He represented the second generation of a highly artistic American family: John William Hill's own son John Henry Hill would also become an outstanding watercolor landscape artist. The work of John William Hill almost spanned the century. He absorbed influences from the academic style of William Guy Wall to the pre-Raphaelite influences of Ruskin and Turner in the last part of the century. In his best work, Hill achieved some of the most impressive representations in American topographical painting. Attention to fine detail without loss of overall design, masterful composition, and wonderful understanding of the myriad effects of light and atmosphere in landscape set his watercolor views apart. Translation of these watercolors to prints had varying degrees of success, however. One of Hill's most spectacular watercolors views of Boston Harbor suffers in the print from its tightly clenched "banknote" engraving by Charles Mottram. The spontaneity of the watercolor is lost and the composition damaged by the arbitrary insertion by the engraver of a large "modern" three-masted ship. Several church spires are caught in the engraver's web of the ship's rigging, and clearly stated compositional lines from foreground figures to the central detail of the Boston State House dome are broken. Hill collaborated with many different engravers during his artistic career, and few captured the distinctive qualities of Hill's original work. A group of early Hill watercolors in the Stokes Collection of the New York Public Library, done in the early 1830's, are excellent examples of Hill's remarkable sophistication of artistic vision and his adroit rendering in watercolor, although the artist was still a very young man. Painted before Hill was twenty years old, these

PLATE 3   Photograph of Hill Studio in Nyack, New York. Hand colored and signed by J. H. Hill, 1910. Graphic Arts Collection. Gift of The Old Print Shop.

American scenes have the same mastery of form and the nuances of light and color that distinguishes the city views of such English masters of topographic art as Thomas Girtin (1775-1802) and Thomas Shotter Boys (1803-1874).

In fact, the high degree of artistry and refinement apparent in both Bennett's aquatints and John William Hill's watercolors must be seen as an American flowering of the rich Eng-

lish landscape tradition. A more indigenous American tradition in painting had been asserting itself ever since the establishment of the Hudson River School by Thomas Cole and his compatriots, but European traditions remained far more entrenched in American printmaking.

In spite of several distinctively American engravers in both copper and wood, a pervasively American expression in the depiction in print of its own surrounding landscape did not really make itself evident in a national sense until the advent and spread of lithography in American prints of the last half of the century.

Lithography, involving the far easier making of images by drawing directly on the lithographic stone, was introduced to this country by Bass Otis in a small landscape printed in 1819. By the 1840's lithography was in common use, and after mid-century began to take its place as a great American popular art form. Finally, following the Civil War, chromolithography burst forth with all the dazzle and color that Currier & Ives of New York and Louis Prang of Boston could muster. Only photography would supersede lithography as the ultimate democratic art form. Lithographic city views became after mid-century one of the most important subjects of printmakers. In the period between 1850 and 1870 a compulsive desire to record the image of every American town seemed to grip the conscience and energies of several artists and print publishers. In these lithographed cities—"America on Stone," as Harry Peters implies in the title of his monumental history of American lithography—a pictorial chronicle of a swiftly changing America is recorded. The pastoral view of America, so beautifully set forth with the early *Hudson River Port Folio* and culminating in many ways in the watercolors of George Harvey and John William Hill, began to vanish. New modes of trans-

PLATE 4   Boston, 1853. Watercolor by John William Hill. [Cat. No. 73]. Graphic Arts Collection. Gift of Leonard L. Milberg '53.

PLATE 5   Boston, 1857. Engraving after John William Hill. [Cat. No. 74]. Graphic Arts Collection. Gift of Leonard L. Milberg '53.

portation, first canals and steamboats, then roads and railroads, accommodated pioneer zeal for ever more rapid movement and ever more settlement of the American continent. *The Literary World* of May 8, 1847, in a review of an exhibition of American landscapes, included some prophetic observations: "The axe of civilization is busy with our old forests, and artisan ingenuity is fast sweeping away relics of our national infancy . . . it behooves our artists to rescue . . . the little that is left, before it is forever too late."

One of the most active artists to take this message to heart was Edwin Whitefield (1816-1892). Travelling throughout the eastern United States and Canada, Whitefield recorded what he saw in an incredible number of sketchbooks, watercolors and lithographs. Whitefield pursued financial success in the form of subscription lists, but he also inspired early interest in the architectural preservation of early American houses in his *Homes of Our Forefathers* (1879).

Regional artists of city views also emerged in lithographs of the 1850's. The most remarkable of a group of provincial folk artists of their own home towns was Henry Walton (1804-1865). Closely associated with Ithaca, New York, and its surrounding area, Walton's lithographs are intimate, closely observed scenes full of deftly rendered details of farm animals, neighbors' houses, and highly decorative figures on country-road parade.

Fitz Hugh Lane (1804-1865) worked chiefly in the Boston area, and created some of the most attractive lithograph views of the nineteenth century in his 1855 prints of Gloucester harbor and Castine, Maine. Both prints reveal the interest in light that made Lane one of the leaders of the Luminist school of American landscape painters.

Two itinerant artists working in this period and both char-acterized by exhaustive eagerness to chronicle everything they saw on their extensive travels were John Warner Barber (1798-1885) and Augustus Kollner (1813-1906). Barber called himself "The Picture Preacher" and travelled throughout New England and New Jersey engraving small wood blocks to illustrate his "Historical Collections," which managed to include nearly every small town of the eastern states. Less rustic in his pictorial chronicle of the American scene, but equally indefatigable as a travelling artist, Augustus Kollner drew sketches of cities and scenery throughout Pennsylvania, New Jersey and New York, as well as Delaware, Maryland, Virginia and Ohio.

Western expansion created its own group of travelling artists. Scenes on the Mississippi have beautiful delineation in the work of the Swiss artist Karl Bodmer and in the illustrations of Henry Lewis's *Das Illustrierte Mississippithal* of 1854. Farther west, Alfred E. Mathews (1831-1874), Kuchel and Dresel, and Britton and Rey were quick to record the opening of the frontier in a multitude of eyewitness scenes printed in lithography.

The decade of 1850-1860 thus produced a generation of new American topographical artists all working for the flourishing lithographic print trade. This grand pictorial chronicle of the American scene was only a small proportion, however, of print subjects compared to the prints made of the greatest city of them all, New York. The strong interest in scenes of life in New York spawned a large number of genre city street scenes that form a different class of views from the typical horizon perspectives. Still another form of city portrait, the "bird's-eye" view, which has its own long history in European prints, also assumed an extraordinary new popularity in American prints of the last half of the century. These views, in which the entire cityscape is tilted sharply to a new angle of vision, show little or no sky and move far closer to map format than pictorial scene. Such prints often reject aesthetic concerns in favor of topographical information. The sky, so important in earlier American views, becomes minimal to non-existent.

The ultimate factual recorder of the American scene, the camera, had begun to replace the practical need of engraved and lithographed city views early in the 1850's. Mathew Brady's Daguerrian Gallery is shown in the Hill-Papprill New York engraving of 1849, and a photographer with his box camera and tripod is included as a conspicuous foreground figure in a lithograph panorama of Albany of 1852. The lithographer, Eliphalet M. Brown, also announced in the label of his print, "Taken from Daguerreotypes."

American city views, from the earliest engraved panoramas to modern photographs, form a class of prints of endless interest and importance beyond the merely decorative. While often beautiful, the prints also formed an important part of an emerging national identity for a young, still insecure country. In historical context, they became our collective cards of identity, and one of the best of all documentary records of how we have seen ourselves. All historical prints, in their wonderful multiplicity, reveal to the inquiring eye not only many factual details of the way things were, but also the way the most professional of observers, the artist, interpreted life and the world around us.

As a young collector of American prints, Leonard Milberg has been able to find fine impressions, in excellent condition, of some of the most important and rarest of historical American views. His personal collection now begins to parallel the great I. N. Phelps Stokes Collection of city views in the New York

PLATE 6   Detail from View of Albany, Capitol of the Empire State . . . , 1852. Lithograph by Eliphalet M. Brown, Jr. [Cat. No. 99]. Graphic Arts Collection. Gift of Leonard L. Milberg '53.

Public Library, both in direction and in representation. Here at Princeton, Leonard has demonstrated unfailing generosity in also helping the Graphic Arts Collection to form an outstanding collection of American historical prints. The city views he has given greatly expand the already strong American holdings of the Princeton University Library. Princeton's Sinclair Hamilton Collection of Early American Book Illustrators and Wood Engravers, 1670-1870, has almost unrivaled representation of its subject, and the Graphic Arts Collection of nineteenth- and twentieth-century American prints, mainly formed by Elmer Adler, gives extensive representation of more recent times. The Milberg gifts to Princeton have not only supplemented these collections in masterful prints of American scenery, but have also included such needed practical assistance as endowment funding for the Graphic Arts Collection and for the printing of this catalogue. More than this, Leonard has proved himself to be an invaluable friend and colleague in the shared pursuit of American art in prints and drawings.

Dale Roylance
CURATOR, *Graphic Arts Collection*
Princeton University Library

CATALOGUE OF THE EXHIBITION

by Nancy Finlay

EARLY VIEWS

The arts developed slowly in the British colonies in North America, and the seventeenth century and the greater part of the eighteenth century passed before anything like a native topographical tradition began to emerge. The earliest published views were almost all based upon sketches by visiting Englishmen, and were engraved and printed after their return to England to satisfy the widespread curiosity there about the appearance of the New World. One of the finest series of such prints, *The Atlantic Neptune*, was published by the British Admiralty between 1763 and 1784 to provide mariners with accurate depictions of the ports and coastline of North America. More artistic in its intent was the roughly contemporary *Scenographia Americana*, which presented highly dramatic and often slightly exotic renderings of American scenery, interpreted according to the formulas of English romantic landscape painting. All of these early English views were reproduced using the various techniques of copperplate engraving, a combination of line engraving and etching in the *Scenographia Americana*, and delicately shaded aquatints in *The Atlantic Neptune*.

To satisfy European curiosity about the appearance of American cities, other enterprising European printmakers issued European or purely imaginary scenes with American titles. Thus a view of Christopher Wren's Greenwich Hospital (with overtones of Claude Lorrain) was imaginatively transformed into Philadelphia, and a high Baroque townscape was passed off as colonial Boston! Such brightly colored popular prints with reversed lettering were meant to be seen in a special tabletop viewer, in which a system of lens and mirror produced the illusion of three dimensions.

By 1800, the art of copperplate engraving was well established in America, but was still primarily applied to the printing of banknotes and paper money. The Revolutionary War inspired a few crude battle scenes, such as Paul Revere's engraving of the Boston Massacre, Amos Doolittle's series of the Battles of Lexington and Concord, and Bernard Romans's "Battle of Charleston," but in these views the accurate depiction of topography was of less importance than the patriotic fervor which the engraver hoped to excite. Following the Revolution, engraved views of American cities began to appear in such publications as the *Columbian Magazine*, the *Massachusetts Magazine*, and the *New York Magazine*.

1. Vue de Boston, c. 1776

Engraved by Franz Xavier Habermann

Habermann's imaginary view of Boston, with its Baroque buildings painted vivid shades of yellow and pink, is a good example of the type of popular print known as the *vue d'optique*.

GRAPHIC ARTS COLLECTION

2. Boston, 1744

Woodcut by James Turner
From The American Magazine, *July 1745*

James Turner's crude woodcut view of Boston, which appeared on the cover of the *American Magazine* in 1744 and 1745, qualifies as one of the earliest native American city views. Woodcuts were easier to carve and print than the more elaborate engravings used to reproduce contemporary English views, and the earliest of all American prints, the famous portrait of Richard Mather by John Foster, was executed as a woodcut as early as 1670. The technique did not allow for fine detail, however, and since such prints were generally small in size, it was not really well adapted for topographical views.

3. A S.W. VIEW OF THE STATE HOUSE IN BOSTON, 1793

Line engraving by Samuel Hill
From The Massachusetts Magazine, *July 1793*

"[This] large and elegant plate . . . forms the finest view that we have ever offered to our generous patrons," the editors of the *Massachusetts Magazine* proudly announced in July 1793. Despite its relative crudity, compared to contemporary English work, Hill's engraving of the Boston State House, with its careful attention to architectural detail and its new fascination with the contemporary life of the city, marks a great advance over Turner's generalized representation of the skyline, quaint Indians and implausible palm tree.

SCENOGRAPHIA AMERICANA

This important series of engraved views of American cities and scenery was issued in London in 1768. Very few artists in America—a mere handful—were capable of either engraving or printing metal plates at this early date, and none was capable of the degree of sophistication and elaboration achieved in these English works. Although technically the title *Scenographia Americana* applies only to a set of twenty-eight prints, it is often used to include a much larger group of similar views issued by the same publisher at about the same time. Since the views were all engraved in England from the sketches of amateurs by artists who had never visited the New World, many of them are highly romanticized and strongly influenced by the artists' preconceived ideas of the great American wilderness.

4. A VIEW OF THE FALLS OF THE PASSAICK . . . , 1768

Sketched by Thomas Pownall
Etched by Paul Sandby
Published by John Bowles, Robert Sayer, Thomas Jefferys,
Carington Bowles and Henry Parker

Paul Sandby (1725-1809), who etched many of the best plates in *Scenographia Americana,* helped to establish the romantic landscape tradition in Britain through his many paintings of wild scenery in Scotland and Wales. His rendering of Thomas Pownall's sketch of Passaic Falls in what is now Paterson, New Jersey, admirably suggests the vastness of the American landscape, with its tiny figures dwarfed in comparison to the natural spectacle they contemplate.

5. A SOUTH-EAST VIEW OF NEW YORK, in NORTH AMERICA, 1768

Drawn by Thomas Howdell

Engraved by Pierre Canot

Published by John Bowles, Robert Sayer, Thomas Jefferys, Carington Bowles and Henry Parker

Because he never visited New York himself, and evidently imagined it a tropical paradise, Pierre Canot interpreted the large tree in the foreground of Captain Thomas Howdell's sketch as a palm tree in his engraving for *Scenographia Americana*. This is the earliest known view of King's College (now Columbia University), founded in 1754, the large building appearing in the background.

GRAPHIC ARTS COLLECTION

THE CITY OF PHILADELPHIA

A milestone in the development of the American city view, *The City of Philadelphia . . . As It Appeared in the Year 1800*, was the first series of such views produced and published entirely in the United States. William Russell Birch (1755-1834), his son Thomas Birch (1779-1851) and Samuel Seymour (fl. 1796-1823) were responsible for drawing, engraving and printing the twenty-eight plates of the first edition, published in Philadelphia in 1800. These lively street scenes convey a vivid sense of the bustle and importance of the city at that time. While many views by Europeans continue to concentrate on the wilder aspects of American scenery and to portray American cities nestled in their landscape settings, the Birches were proud to represent Philadelphia as a worthy rival to London, Paris and the other great cities of Europe.

The first two plates are from the first edition of 1800. This edition, which quickly sold out, was followed in 1804 by a second edition, including thirteen plates from the first edition and seven new ones. The rather desolate view of the interior of the High Street Market was one of those plates which was replaced, in the second edition, by a much livelier scene. *High Street from the Country Market-Place* and *Second Street, North from Market Street* are both prints which first appeared in the 1804 edition. A third and final edition of an assortment of plates was issued in 1827-28. The success of Birch's venture foretokened the popularity which the city view was to enjoy in nineteenth-century America.

PLATE 7   The City of Philadelphia in the State of Pennsylvania North America, 1801. Engraving after Thomas Birch. [Cat. No. 6].
Leonard L. Milberg Collection.

6. THE CITY OF PHILADELPHIA IN THE STATE OF PENNSYLVANIA NORTH AMERICA, 1801

Drawn by Thomas Birch
Engraved by Samuel Seymour
Published by William Birch and William H. Morgan

An enlarged and more elaborate version of the frontispiece of Birch's book, *The City of Philadelphia*, this print was issued independently in 1801. The large tree at the right was believed to be the elm under which William Penn concluded his treaty with the Indians in 1681. Because it served as the nation's capital from 1790 to 1800, Philadelphia is probably the best documented American city of the Federal period.

LEONARD L. MILBERG COLLECTION

7. HIGH STREET MARKET, PHILADELPHIA, 1799

Drawn, engraved and published by William and Thomas Birch

GRAPHIC ARTS COLLECTION
GIFT OF WILLIAM PRICKETT '47

8. ARCH STREET WITH THE SECOND PRESBYTERIAN CHURCH, PHILADELPHIA, 1799

Drawn, engraved and published by William and Thomas Birch

GRAPHIC ARTS COLLECTION
GIFT OF WILLIAM PRICKETT '47

9. HIGH STREET, FROM THE COUNTRY MARKET-PLACE, PHILADELPHIA WITH THE PROCESSION IN COMMEMORATION OF THE DEATH OF GENERAL GEORGE WASHINGTON, DECEMBER 26th, 1799

Drawn and published by William Birch

GRAPHIC ARTS COLLECTION
GIFT OF WILLIAM PRICKETT '47

10. SECOND STREET, NORTH FROM MARKET ST. W^{TH.} CHRIST CHURCH, PHILADELPHIA, 1800

Drawn and published by William Birch

GRAPHIC ARTS COLLECTION
GIFT OF WILLIAM PRICKETT '47

PLATE 8   View of St. Anthony's Nose in the North River, Province of New York, 1795. Aquatint after G. B. Fisher. [Cat. No. 13].
Leonard L. Milberg Collection.

ALEXANDER ROBERTSON (1772-1841)

Robertson was born in Aberdeen, Scotland and trained in London before coming to New York in 1792 and founding the Columbian Academy of Painting, one of America's first art schools, where he and his brother Archibald taught drawing in watercolor for reproduction in aquatint. As there were still no aquatint engravers active in America, these drawings were sent abroad for reproduction. Francis Jukes (1746-1812), who engraved both of the views shown here, was an early English aquatint engraver, who strove to capture the effect of the original watercolor drawings in his prints, using extensive hand-coloring applied in flat washes over the delicate shading produced by the aquatint process.

11. HUDSONS RIVER FROM CHAMBERS CREEK LOOKING THRO' THE HIGH LANDS, 1802

Drawn by Alexander Robertson
Engraved in aquatint by Francis Jukes
Published by Jukes and Robertson

LEONARD L. MILBERG COLLECTION

12. PASSAIC FALLS IN THE STATE OF NEW JERSEY, 1802

Drawn by Alexander Robertson
Engraved in aquatint by Francis Jukes
Published by Jukes and Robertson

LEONARD L. MILBERG COLLECTION

EUROPEAN VISITORS

Even following the American Revolution, many American views were produced by British artists and printed and published by British publishers. G. B. Fisher and George Beck were among the first of a long line of itinerant topographical painters who travelled widely in search of picturesque subjects. Fisher was active in northern New York State and eastern Canada; Beck, who emigrated to America in 1795, worked primarily in Maryland and Pennsylvania. The Atkins and Nightingale series of American views, based on Beck's drawings, were published in London in 1801-1809. Other European artists contributed heavily to the American iconographic tradition in the early years of the nineteenth century. In 1819-20, Swedish nobleman Axel Klinckowström sketched two New York views which were engraved in aquatint to accompany his *Letters from the United States*, published in Stockholm in 1824. Frenchman Jacques Gérard Milbert spent nine years in America from 1815 to 1824, and after his return to Paris published two books, *Picturesque Views of North America* (1825) and *Itinéraire Pittoresque du Fleuve Hudson* (1828-1829), illustrated with lithographs after his drawings.

13. VIEW OF ST. ANTHONY'S NOSE IN THE NORTH RIVER, PROVINCE OF NEW YORK, 1795

Drawn by G. B. Fisher
Engraved in aquatint by J. W. Edy
Published by J. W. Edy

G. B. Fisher was the artist of a number of views of Eastern Canada in the 1790's, as well as of a painting of Niagara Falls in the Victoria and Albert Museum in London. This aquatint of Anthony's Nose with its tranquil calm and lovely silvery gray tonality is one of the most beautiful early views of the Hudson (also known as the North River in the eighteenth century).

LEONARD L. MILBERG COLLECTION

14. GREAT FALLS OF THE POTOMAC, 1802

Drawn by George Beck
Engraved in aquatint by T. Cartwright
Published by Atkins and Nightingale

Besides views of Niagara and the Great Falls of the Potomac, the Atkins and Nightingale series of aquatint views includes a number of American cities such as Philadelphia, Washington, and Baltimore, all of great interest because of their early date.

LEONARD L. MILBERG COLLECTION

15. BRODWAY-GATAN OCH RÅDHUSET I NEWYORK (BROADWAY AND CITY HALL IN NEW YORK), 1824

Drawn by Axel Klinckowström
Engraved by Akrell

This charming view of New York, c. 1819, shows a picturesque small city of quiet shady streets. The remarkably elegant and fashionable passersby contrast with the pigs rooting along the gutters. The fact that pigs were allowed to run loose in the city streets was often commented upon unfavorably by early visitors to New York.

GRAPHIC ARTS COLLECTION

16. NEWYORKS HAMN OCH REDD FRÅN BROOKLYN PÅ LONGISLAND (NEW YORK HARBOR AND DOCKS FROM BROOKLYN ON LONG ISLAND)

Drawn by Axel Klinckowström
Engraved by Akrell

Other views accompanying Baron Klinckowström's *Letters from the United States* depicted scenes in Philadelphia, Washington, and Hoboken, New Jersey.

GRAPHIC ARTS COLLECTION

17. BRO ÖFVER SCHUYLKILL STROMMEN NÄRA PHILADELPHIA (BRIDGE OVER THE SCHUYLKILL RIVER AT PHILADELPHIA)

Drawn by Axel Klinckowström
Engraved by Akrell

Klinckowström's view of the "Schuylkill Permanent Bridge," the longest wooden span in the world at the time of its construction in 1800-1805, was directly copied from a painting by Thomas Birch now in the Historical Society of Pennsylvania. In that time of less stringent copyright laws, artists often copied or adapted one another's compositions. Several other examples of this practice are to be seen in this exhibition.

DEPARTMENT OF RARE BOOKS
GIFT OF PROFESSOR ERIK SJÖQVIST

18. Itinéraire Pittoresque du Fleuve Hudson et des Parties Latérales, 1828-29

Written and illustrated by Jacques Gérard Milbert
Lithographed by Adam, Bichebois, Deroy, Dupressoir, Jacottet, Joly, Sabatier, Tirpenne & Villeneuve
Published by Henry Gaugain & Cie., Paris

Jacques Gérard Milbert (1766-1840) came to the United States in 1815 on a scientific mission for the French government and remained until 1823, painting portraits and landscapes and teaching drawing in New York City. While in New York, he was involved with the planning commission for the Erie Canal, and in this connection made the voyage up the Hudson which is recorded in his *Itinéraire Pittoresque*. This portfolio, published after his return to France, contains city views of New York, Albany and Saratoga Springs as well as picturesque landscapes similar in conception to contemporary works by Hill and Bennett—plus the inevitable panoramas of Niagara Falls.

GRAPHIC ARTS COLLECTION
GIFT OF LEONARD L. MILBERG '53

19. Vue de Boston prise du Pont du Sud (View of Boston and the South Boston Bridge)

Drawn by Jacques Gérard Milbert
Lithographed by Deroy

LEONARD L. MILBERG COLLECTION

20. Vue de New York prise de Weahawk—A View of New York Taken from Veahawk, c. 1834

Painted by Ambroise Louis Garneray
Engraved by Sigmund Himely

Ambroise Louis Garneray (1783-1857) was a French marine painter in the Romantic tradition of Joseph Vernet. Since Garneray never visited the United States himself, he must have consulted prints or drawings by other artists for this view of the New York skyline, and in fact the background of Garneray's aquatint is very similar to that in the "Vue de New York prise de Weahawk" in Jacques Gérard Milbert's recently published *Itinéraire Pittoresque du Fleuve Hudson* and was probably copied from it. Garneray's view first appeared in his *Vues des Côtes de France dans l'Océan et dans la Méditerranée* (Paris: 1830-35), the final volume of which included a few aquatint engravings of American ports.

LEONARD L. MILBERG COLLECTION

JOHN HILL (1770-1850)

Aquatint engraving developed in England in the late eighteenth century. Combined with etched or engraved lines, aquatint was used to produce half-tones. The prints were then hand-colored and the results often bear a striking resemblance to the watercolor drawings they were intended to imitate. The technique was difficult and laborious; it was not unusual for two or three engravers to be employed on a single plate, with one man responsible for the etching, another for the aquatint, and so on. Considerable technical training was involved, and it is not surprising that the best American aquatint engravers were born and educated in England and were already accomplished artists when they emigrated to the United States. John Hill is a good example of this phenomenon. He was active in London as an engraver of views after J.M.W. Turner and other romantic landscape artists before emigrating to this country in 1816, where he soon found employment engraving similar views of American subjects. His *Picturesque Views of American Scenery*, after paintings by Joshua Shaw, was published in Philadelphia in 1820. The *Hudson River Port Folio*, probably his masterpiece, was engraved from paintings by William Guy Wall, and appeared in parts between 1820 and 1825. The engraver John Hill was the father of John William Hill, whose views of American cities were much reproduced by later lithographers.

21. PASSAIC FALLS, NEW JERSEY

Painted by Joshua Shaw
Engraved in aquatint by John Hill
Published by M. Carey & Son, Philadelphia

This view from Shaw's *Picturesque Views of American Scenery* (1820) should be compared to the eighteenth-century version of the same scene from *Scenographia Americana*; its "picturesque" detail and more intimate and human scale contrast with the sublime and savage character of the earlier work.

GRAPHIC ARTS COLLECTION
GIFT OF LEONARD L. MILBERG '53

22. VIEW OF THE SPOT WHERE GEN. ROSS FELL NEAR BALTIMORE

Painted by Joshua Shaw
Engraved in aquatint by John Hill
Published by M. Carey & Son, Philadelphia

Another view from *Picturesque Views of American Scenery*, this print commemorates an event from the recent War of 1812. General Ross, the British officer responsible for the burning of Washington, was killed while attacking Baltimore in 1814.

LEONARD L. MILBERG COLLECTION

PLATE 9   Passaic Falls, New Jersey, 1820. Aquatint by John Hill. [Cat. No. 21]. Graphic Arts Collection. Gift of Leonard L. Milberg '53.

23. HELL GATE

Painted by Joshua Shaw
Engraved in aquatint by John Hill
Published by M. Carey & Son, Philadelphia

This tranquil landscape from *Picturesque Views of American Scenery* portrays the treacherous shoals at the mouth of New York's East River.

LEONARD L. MILBERG COLLECTION

24. BOLLING'S DAM, PETERSBURGH, VIRGINIA

Painted by Joshua Shaw
Engraved in aquatint by John Hill
Published by M. Carey & Son, Philadelphia

Shaw's decision to include a view of this small Virginia town in his *Picturesque Views of American Scenery* may also have been prompted by the prominent role played by its volunteers during the War of 1812, when they earned for Petersburg the proud name of the "Cockade City."

LEONARD L. MILBERG COLLECTION

25. VIEW NEAR HUDSON

No. 12 of the Hudson River Port Folio
Painted by William Guy Wall
Engraved in aquatint by John Hill
Published by Henry J. Megarey

The *Hudson River Port Folio*, containing twenty aquatint engravings by John Hill after watercolor paintings by William Guy Wall, was published in parts between 1820 and 1825. It was clearly an attempt to rival contemporary English colorplate books, and in fact both Wall and Hill had recently emigrated from England. During the next decades, painters such as Thomas Cole and Asher B. Durand would be attracted by the picturesque beauty of the Hudson River Valley, producing the so-called "Hudson River School" of American painting (See Plate 1).

GRAPHIC ARTS COLLECTION
GIFT OF LEONARD L. MILBERG '53

26. WEST POINT

No. 16 of the Hudson River Port Folio
Painted by William Guy Wall
Engraved in aquatint by John Hill
Published by Henry J. Megarey

This rather stark, gloomy landscape contrasts with William James Bennett's sunnier renderings of the same site. The steamboat on the river is a recurring motif, appearing in several separate plates of the *Hudson River Port Folio*.

LEONARD L. MILBERG COLLECTION

27. PALISADES

No. 19 of the Hudson River Port Folio
Painted by William Guy Wall
Engraved in aquatint by John Hill
Published by Henry J. Megarey

In the second state of this print, the steamboat in the foreground bears the name *Clermont*, commemorating Robert Fulton's original vessel with that name, which steamed up the Hudson from New York City to Albany in 1807, demonstrating the feasibility of steam-powered navigation. Artists of the day loved to glorify such technological achievements, and although Hill's engraving dates from almost twenty years after the *Clermont*'s maiden voyage, it reflects some of the excitement of the early days of steam.

LEONARD L. MILBERG COLLECTION

28. NEW YORK, FROM GOVERNOR'S ISLAND

No. 20 of the Hudson River Port Folio
Painted by William Guy Wall
Engraved in aquatint by John Hill
Published by Henry J. Megarey

Unlike Milbert's *Itinéraire Pittoresque du Fleuve Hudson*, which charted the artist's voyage *up* the river, the twenty plates of the *Hudson River Port Folio* trace the river's course from its headwaters to the sea. This view of New York harbor, at the mouth of the Hudson, is the final plate in the series.

LEONARD L. MILBERG COLLECTION

29. CITY HALL, 1826

Drawn by William Guy Wall
Engraved, printed and colored by John Hill
Published by Behr & Kahl

This aquatint by John Hill depicts the New York City Hall erected in 1803-1812 to the designs of Joseph F. Mangin and John McComb, Jr. Images such as this one celebrate the monumental new civic buildings that were rising to rival the palaces of Europe throughout the eastern United States in the early years of the nineteenth century.

LEONARD L. MILBERG COLLECTION

30. FAIR MOUNT WATER WORKS

Painted by Thomas Doughty
Engraved, printed and colored by John Hill
Published by H. C. Carey & I. Lea, Philadelphia and H. J. Megarey, New York

Designed by architect William Strickland and engineer Frederick Graff in the early years of the nineteenth century, the Fairmount Waterworks charmingly combined the practical with the picturesque. Hill's aquatint engraving after Thomas Doughty (1793-1850), one of the founders of the Hudson River School, suggests the direct connection between the pastoral vision of the earlier British-trained generation of artists, represented by Hill, and that of the first important native American school.

GRAPHIC ARTS COLLECTION
GIFT OF LEONARD L. MILBERG '53

NIAGARA FALLS, PART OF THE AMERICAN FALL FROM THE FOOT OF THE STAIR CASE

Painted by William James Bennett
Engraved in aquatint by John Hill
Published by Henry J. Megarey

See Catalogue No. 56.

NIAGARA FALLS, PART OF THE BRITISH FALL, TAKEN FROM UNDER THE TABLE ROCK

Painted by William James Bennett
Engraved in aquatint by John Hill
Published by Henry J. Megarey

See Catalogue No. 57.

ALBANY FROM GREENBUSH, 1834

Drawn by John William Hill
Engraved in aquatint by John Hill
Published by Betts & Anstice

See Catalogue No. 70.

31. A SHOAL OF SPERM WHALE OFF THE ISLAND OF HAWAII, 1838

Drawn by Cornelius B. Hulsart
Painted by Thomas Birch
Engraved, printed and colored by John Hill
Published by Cornelius B. Hulsart

This whaling print, engraved by John Hill from a painting by Thomas Birch, affords a distant glimpse of the island of Hawaii in the 1830's. Aside from his important contributions to *The City of Philadelphia* (Cat. Nos. 6-10), Birch was responsible for relatively few city views, specializing instead in harbor scenes, seascapes and paintings of naval battles, such as *The Engagement between the "Constitution" and the "Guerriere"* of 1812.

LEONARD L. MILBERG COLLECTION

WILLIAM HENRY BARTLETT (1809-1854)

The English topographical artist William Henry Bartlett made four visits to the United States making sketches for *American Scenery* by Nathaniel Parker Willis, published in two volumes in 1840. These volumes provide a compendium of those American views that had come to be considered characteristically sublime or picturesque, including Niagara Falls, Trenton Falls, the view from West Point, the New Jersey Palisades, as well as views of such cities as Boston, New York and Washington.

32. AMERICAN SCENERY, LONDON, 1840

By Nathaniel Parker Willis
Illustrated with steel engravings after William Henry Bartlett

GRAPHIC ARTS COLLECTION

GEORGE HARVEY (c. 1800-1878)

George Harvey came to America from England about 1820 and travelled extensively in Ohio, Michigan and Canada before establishing himself as an artist in New York, eventually building a home near Washington Irving's "Sunnyside" on the Hudson. His project to publish a portfolio of forty views failed for lack of financial backing, and only four prints were issued, as *Harvey's Scenes of the Primitive Forest of America* in 1841, engraved in aquatint by William James Bennett. Each view centers on a dramatic incident: an accident with a hay wagon, an ox cart crossing a ford, combining the interest of a rural genre scene with the depiction of the "primitive forest." Despite Harvey's title, these are less scenes of untamed wilderness than they are representations of the interaction between man and nature in the period of westward expansion.

33. A ROAD ACCIDENT, A GLIMPSE THRO' AN OPENING OF THE PRIMITIVE FOREST, THORNVILLE, OHIO

Painted by George Harvey
Engraved in aquatint by William James Bennett

LEONARD L. MILBERG COLLECTION

34. BURNING FALLEN TREES IN A GIRDLED CLEARING, WESTERN SCENE

Painted by George Harvey
Engraved in aquatint by William James Bennett

LEONARD L. MILBERG COLLECTION

35. GIGANTIC SYCAMORES, AN OX TEAM CROSSING THE FORD, OWL CREEK, OHIO

Painted by George Harvey

LEONARD L. MILBERG COLLECTION

36. IMPEDED TRAVELLERS IN A PINE FOREST, UPPER CANADA

Painted by George Harvey

LEONARD L. MILBERG COLLECTION

WILLIAM JAMES BENNETT (1787-1844)

A contemporary of John Hill, William James Bennett was also born and trained in England, where he exhibited romantic landscapes, including views of Naples and the Barbary Coast, between 1808 and 1825. By 1826, he was settled in New York City. In America, he was primarily active as an engraver of works after other artists, including George Cooke, John William Hill and John Gadsby Chapman, but he also composed aquatints from his own sketches. Compositionally and technically, his prints compare favorably with the best English work of the period. The American topographical tradition is firmly established in the work of Bennett, and later artists would continue to rely on many of the same compositional devices and stock accessories that Bennett employed in his prints on so many occasions. Despite this slightly conventional flavor, however, Bennett's views are among the most memorable images of American cities from the 1830's—a dazzling and sunny vision of the new Republic—and, at their best, they go far beyond mere topographical description to emerge as landscapes and seascapes of great beauty in their own right.

PLATE 10   Boston, from City Point, near Sea Street, 1833. Aquatint by William James Bennett. [Cat. No. 40]. Leonard L. Milberg Collection.

19

37. BALTIMORE FROM FEDERAL HILL, 1831

Painted and engraved in aquatint by William James Bennett
Printed by J. & G. Neale
Published by Henry J. Megarey

This lovely view of Baltimore is one of a pair of prints Bennett composed from his own sketches, made during a visit to Baltimore in 1830. The animated genre elements in the foreground and the daring perspective of the row houses and wharves in the middle ground combined with the glistening panorama of the city across the river make this one of Bennett's most attractive views.

LEONARD L. MILBERG COLLECTION

38. BALTIMORE TAKEN NEAR WHETSTONE POINT, 1831

Painted and engraved in aquatint by William James Bennett
Printed by J. & G. Neale
Published by Henry J. Megarey

Sepia proof before letters of the second of Bennett's two views of Baltimore.

I. N. PHELPS STOKES COLLECTION
THE NEW YORK PUBLIC LIBRARY
ASTOR, LENOX AND TILDEN FOUNDATION

39. WEST POINT, FROM PHILLIPSTOWN, 1831

Painted and engraved in aquatint by William James Bennett
Published by Parker & Clover

The inscription at the lower left, "Coloured by Hill," documents an early collaboration between the two aquatint engravers. The silvery gray tonality of this print should be contrasted to the brighter, almost garish coloring of *West Point, from above Washington Valley*, also in the exhibition (Cat. No. 43).

LEONARD L. MILBERG COLLECTION

40. BOSTON, FROM CITY POINT, NEAR SEA STREET, 1833

Painted and engraved in aquatint by William James Bennett
Published by Henry J. Megarey

In an announcement issued by Lewis P. Clover in 1837, this print and its companion print "engraved on copper in the best manner and beautifully colored" were offered for sale at $5.00 apiece.

LEONARD L. MILBERG COLLECTION

41. Boston from the Ship House, West End of the Navy Yard, 1833

Painted and engraved by William James Bennett
Published by Henry J. Megarey

A modern restrike printed in 1901 by the Club of Odd Volumes from the original Bennett aquatint plate, this copy lacks the hand-coloring that makes most of Bennett's views so attractive.

LEONARD L. MILBERG COLLECTION

42. Richmond, from the Hill above the Waterworks, 1834

Painted by George Cooke
Engraved in aquatint by William James Bennett
Published by Lewis P. Clover

The fruitful association of George Cooke and William James Bennett appears to have begun in 1834, when Lewis P. Clover issued a series of views engraved by Bennett from paintings by Cooke. Cooke was an American artist, born in St. Mary's County, Maryland in 1793. He travelled widely throughout the Eastern United States, painting portraits and historical compositions as well as landscapes, dying in New Orleans in 1849.

LEONARD L. MILBERG COLLECTION

43. West Point, from above Washington Valley, 1834

Painted by George Cooke
Engraved in aquatint by William James Bennett
Published by Parker & Clover

George Cooke's view of West Point on the Hudson belongs to the romantic landscape tradition established in the eighteenth-century prints of *Scenographia Americana* and continued in the *Hudson River Port Folio* of John Hill. Currier & Ives later issued a lithograph based on this print.

GRAPHIC ARTS COLLECTION
GIFT OF LEONARD L. MILBERG '53

44. City of Washington from beyond the Navy Yard, 1834

Painted by George Cooke
Engraved in aquatint by William James Bennett
Published by Lewis P. Clover

Washington is still quite a small town in this lovely Bennett view from 1834, showing the infant capital nestling in the midst of a romanticized countryside. The two large buildings are the White House, at the left, and the Capitol, at the right.

LEONARD L. MILBERG COLLECTION

PLATE 11 West Point, from above Washington Valley, 1834. Aquatint by William James Bennett. [Cat. No. 43].
Graphic Arts Collection. Gift of Leonard L. Milberg '53.

FULTON ST. & MARKET, 1834

Painted and engraved in aquatint by William James Bennett
Published by Henry J. Megarey

See Catalogue No. 67.

45. VIEW OF THE HIGH FALLS OF TRENTON, WEST CANADA CREEK, N.Y., 1835

Painted and engraved in aquatint by William James Bennett
Published by Lewis P. Clover

Trenton Falls, near the village of Trenton, New York, were a popular stopover for nineteenth-century travellers on their way to Niagara, in search of the sublime and picturesque. The dark and rather ominous character of Bennett's view contrasts with the lightness and brightness of his views of Niagara.

LEONARD L. MILBERG COLLECTION

46. BUFFALO, FROM LAKE ERIE, 1836

Drawn by John William Hill
Painted and engraved in aquatint by William James Bennett
Published by Henry J. Megarey

Bennett worked from a drawing by John William Hill, the young son of aquatint engraver John Hill, to produce this view of Buffalo from Lake Erie.

I. N. PHELPS STOKES COLLECTION
THE NEW YORK PUBLIC LIBRARY
ASTOR, LENOX AND TILDEN FOUNDATION

47. VIEW OF NEW YORK, QUARANTINE STATION, STATEN ISLAND, 1836

Painted and engraved in aquatint by William James Bennett
Printed by J. Neale
Published by Parker & Clover

Some of Bennett's most beautiful engravings are of harbor scenes in which, although the titles suggest that they were conceived as city views, the nautical interest seems far greater than the topographical. These lively scenes of shipping in New York harbor provide a vivid record of the brisk commerce of the era.

LEONARD L. MILBERG COLLECTION

48. NEW YORK, TAKEN FROM THE BAY NEAR BEDLOWS ISLAND, 1836

Painted by John Gadsby Chapman
Engraved in aquatint by William James Bennett
Published by Henry J. Megarey

John Gadsby Chapman (1808-1889) was a pupil of George Cooke. Like many other ambitious young American artists, he wanted to become a historical painter in the grand manner, but his beautiful landscapes, such as this view of New York Bay, engraved by Bennett, are still admired today long after his pretentious historical compositions have been forgotten.

LEONARD L. MILBERG COLLECTION

49. City of Detroit, Michigan, Taken from the Canada Shore near the Ferry, 1837

Drawn by Frederick Grain
Engraved in aquatint by William James Bennett
Published by Henry J. Megarey

Little is known of Frederick Grain, the landscape and panorama artist, who provided the sketches which served as the basis for Bennett's aquatint of a surprisingly flourishing early Detroit.

LEONARD L. MILBERG COLLECTION

50. New York from Brooklyn Heights, 1837

Painted by John William Hill
Engraved in aquatint by William James Bennett
Published by Louis P. Clover

One of the most beautiful early views of New York City was engraved by William James Bennett from a painting by John William Hill. In spite of the faded condition of this copy of the print, the luminosity typical of Bennett's best work is fully apparent, and the composition, with its wealth of foreground detail, is one of Hill's finest, looking forward to his magnificent later view of *New York from the Steeple of St. Paul's Church.*

LEONARD L. MILBERG COLLECTION

51. Troy. Taken from the West Bank of the Hudson, in Front of the United States Arsenal, 1838

Painted and engraved in aquatint by William James Bennett
Published by Henry J. Megarey

In a picturesque setting on the Hudson, Troy, New York had already been depicted by William Guy Wall and John Hill in their *Hudson River Port Folio* before Bennett chose to include it among the cities portrayed in his series of American views. It was to remain one of the standard sites for topographical artists throughout the nineteenth century. The mid-century lithographers Whitefield and Kollner both produced views of Troy.

I. N. PHELPS STOKES COLLECTION
THE NEW YORK PUBLIC LIBRARY
ASTOR, LENOX AND TILDEN FOUNDATION

52. City of Charleston, S. Carolina, Looking across Cooper's River, 1838

Painted by George Cooke
Engraved in aquatint by William James Bennett
Published by Lewis P. Clover

Many of Bennett's later engravings are of Southern cities that he never visited. Produced from paintings by other artists, such as his frequent collaborator George Cooke, Bennett's renderings of such cities as Charleston, Mobile, and New Orleans are as faithful and vivid as those relying on his own sketches. One is left with the impression that, whatever artist Bennett copied, his plates were colored by his own romantic vision of the young Republic.

53. NEW ORLEANS, TAKEN FROM THE OPPOSITE SIDE A SHORT DISTANCE ABOVE THE MIDDLE OR PICAYUNE FERRY, 1841

Sketched by Antoine Mondelli
Painted and engraved in aquatint by William James Bennett
Published by Henry J. Megarey

Bennett's view of New Orleans, a city which, like Charleston, he never visited, is based on a sketch by Antoine Mondelli, a local New Orleans artist and scene painter, active from 1821 to 1856.

54. MOBILE. TAKEN FROM THE MARSH OPPOSITE THE CITY NEAR PINTO'S RESIDENCE, 1842

Drawn by William Todd
Painted and engraved in aquatint by William James Bennett
Published by Henry J. Megarey

Once again Bennett was obliged to work from a sketch by another artist, in this case William Todd, for this view of Mobile, Alabama, one of the Southern cities that he included in his series of American views. This proof before letters has been printed in green in preparation for the addition of hand-coloring.

55. A BRISK GALE, BAY OF NEW YORK, 1867

Painted and engraved in aquatint by William James Bennett
Published by George E. Perine

Perhaps the best of Bennett's "nautical" prints is this magnificent late aquatint in which topographical description is almost totally subordinated to the dramatic conflict between man and the elements. Originally published in 1839.

56. NIAGARA FALLS, PART OF THE AMERICAN FALL FROM THE FOOT OF THE STAIR CASE

Painted by William James Bennett
Engraved in aquatint by John Hill
Published by Henry J. Megarey

57. Niagara Falls, Part of the British Fall, Taken from under the Table Rock

Painted by William James Bennett
Engraved in aquatint by John Hill
Published by Henry J. Megarey

The best topographical artists of their day, William James Bennett and John Hill collaborated on these two views of Niagara Falls, with paintings by Bennett providing the basis for the masterful aquatint engravings by Hill. The sublime spectacle of Niagara continued to inspire artists and engravers including Robert Havell, Edwin Whitefield and Augustus Kollner.

GRAPHIC ARTS COLLECTION
GIFT OF LEONARD L. MILBERG '53

NICOLINO CALYO (1799-1884)

A colorful figure who emigrated from Naples in the 1830's, Nicolino Calyo arrived in New York in time to record the catastrophic fire of December 16th and 17th, 1835 in a series of melodramatic views. A pair of these views, showing the conflagration and its aftermath, were reproduced in aquatint by William James Bennett. Calyo also painted portraits and miniatures, scenes from the Mexican War, and other landscape and city views, including a panorama of the Connecticut River.

58. Panoramic View of New York from the North River

Original gouache attributed to Nicolino Calyo

LENT BY THE OLD PRINT SHOP

59. Panoramic View of New York from the East River

Original gouache attributed to Nicolino Calyo

Calyo's two small gouache drawings are closely related to Robert Havell's two similar panoramas of New York (see Cat. Nos. 60 & 61). The relationship between the Calyo drawings and the Havell aquatints is by no means easy to determine; the city skyline is much compressed in the two drawings, but the foreground and boats are almost identical to those in the first state of the print. It is possible that Calyo was somehow involved in making studies for these details. The vessels are attributed to James Pringle in the caption to the print, but this attribution has long been questioned.

LENT BY THE OLD PRINT SHOP

ROBERT HAVELL, JR. (1793-1878)

When John James Audubon went to England in 1826 to find an engraver for *Birds of America*, he selected Robert Havell, Jr. This monumental undertaking occupied the young British engraver from 1827 to 1838; and upon completion of the Audubon plates, Havell decided to emigrate to the United States, settling in Sing Sing (Ossining), New York. Although he was active primarily as a landscape painter during this American period, a few superb colored aquatints of American scenes and cities from the 1840's, mostly after his own paintings, compare favorably with the best work of Hill and Bennett.

60. PANORAMIC VIEW OF NEW YORK (TAKEN FROM THE NORTH RIVER), 1840

Drawn and engraved in aquatint by Robert Havell, Jr.
Published by Robert Havell, Jr.

I. N. PHELPS STOKES COLLECTION
THE NEW YORK PUBLIC LIBRARY
ASTOR, LENOX AND TILDEN FOUNDATION

61. PANORAMIC VIEW OF NEW YORK (TAKEN FROM THE EAST RIVER), 1844

Drawn and engraved in aquatint by Robert Havell, Jr.
Published by Robert Havell, Jr.

By 1840, it was already becoming difficult to encompass all of New York City in a single panoramic view. Havell solved this difficulty by issuing two separate panoramas, one from the East River and another from the Hudson. Later artists would rely increasingly upon bird's-eye views for their sweeping panoramas of the city.

I. N. PHELPS STOKES COLLECTION
THE NEW YORK PUBLIC LIBRARY
ASTOR, LENOX AND TILDEN FOUNDATION

62. NIAGARA FALLS, PAINTED FROM THE CHINESE PAGODA, POINT VIEW GARDENS, 1845

Painted and engraved in aquatint by Robert Havell, Jr.
Printed in colors by W. Neale
Published by L. R. Menger, New York and Ackermann & Co., London

While Bennett concentrated on dramatic close-ups that admirably convey the overwhelming force of the falling water, Robert Havell chose a more distant viewpoint for his panorama of Niagara, in order to suggest the vast extent of the magnificent spectacle, and substituted elegant promenading couples for the rugged hunters of Bennett's engraving.

LEONARD L. MILBERG COLLECTION

PLATE 12   Niagara Falls, Painted from the Chinese Pagoda, Point View Gardens, 1845. Aquatint by Robert Havell, Jr. [Cat. No. 62].
Leonard L. Milberg Collection.

63. VIEW OF THE CITY OF BALTIMORE FROM THE TELEGRAPH, 1847

Painted and engraved in aquatint by Robert Havell, Jr.
Printed by W. Neale
Published by W. A. Colman

Havell's view of Baltimore should be compared to Bennett's earlier view of the same city. Once again the title of the print recalls a recent technological advance: Samuel F. B. Morse sent the first telegraphic message "What hath God wrought!" between Baltimore and Washington, D.C. on May 24, 1844.

LEONARD L. MILBERG COLLECTION

64. VIEW OF WEST POINT UNITED STATES MILITARY ACADEMY, 1848

Painted and engraved in aquatint by Robert Havell, Jr.
Published by L. R. Menger

Havell's use of the aquatint technique should be compared and contrasted to Bennett's and Hill's use of the same medium. While Bennett and Hill composed their views almost entirely in line, using aquatint primarily for shading, Havell's extensive use of pure aquatint, with fewer etched lines, produced delicate atmospheric effects sometimes closely resembling wash drawings.

LEONARD L. MILBERG COLLECTION

JOHN WILLIAM HILL (1812-1879)

John William Hill was the son and pupil of John Hill, the aquatint engraver, and also seems to have been heavily influenced by the work of William James Bennett, with whom the Hills were associated in New York City and afterwards in Nyack. John William Hill was active as a landscape and topographical painter, in contrast to Bennett and his father, who were both primarily engravers of other men's views, and indeed engraved some of the younger Hill's early drawings. By the time John William Hill reached maturity, however, the easier and cheaper technique of lithography was rapidly replacing aquatint engraving for large city views. Hill's most typical works are those city views created for Smith Brothers, the New York lithographic publishers, in the early 1850's, "drawn on stone" by Fanny Palmer and "printed in tints" by Francis Michelin.

65. BROADWAY AND TRINITY CHURCH, NEW YORK, 1830

Watercolor by John William Hill

I. N. PHELPS STOKES COLLECTION
THE NEW YORK PUBLIC LIBRARY
ASTOR, LENOX AND TILDEN FOUNDATION

66. CITY HALL AND PARK ROW, NEW YORK, 1830

Watercolor by John William Hill

These luminous watercolors by the precocious eighteen-year-old artist belong to the same tradition as Birch's earlier city views. They also seem closely related to a similar series of street scenes projected by the New York publisher Henry J. Megarey in the late 1820's, to which William James Bennett contributed three views.

67. FULTON ST. & MARKET, 1834

Painted and engraved in aquatint by William James Bennett
Published by Henry J. Megarey

Bennett's aquatint of *Fulton St. & Market* should be compared to John William Hill's early watercolors of New York street scenes. Bennett's other contributions to Megarey's projected series were *Broadway from the Bowling Green* (c. 1826) and *South Street from Maiden Lane* (c. 1828). These three prints were the only ones in the series that were ever issued.

68. VIEW ON THE ERIE CANAL, 1830-32

Watercolor by John William Hill

69. VIEW OF SCHENECTADY, NEW YORK, 1830-32

Watercolor by John William Hill

Another projected series of views by John William Hill illustrated the sights and cities along the Erie Canal, a symbol of American expansion and progress completed as recently as 1825. Aquatint proofs by the artist's father are known for several of these views which unfortunately were never published.

70. ALBANY FROM GREENBUSH, 1834

Drawn by John William Hill
Engraved in aquatint by John Hill
Published by Betts & Anstice

John William Hill's view of Albany was one of the few designs engraved in aquatint by his father, John Hill. It is a beautiful example of the younger Hill's early work and is closely related to similar views by William James Bennett.

BUFFALO, FROM LAKE ERIE, 1836

Drawn by John William Hill
Painted and engraved in aquatint by William James Bennett
Published by Henry J. Megarey

See Catalogue No. 46.

NEW YORK FROM THE STEEPLE OF
ST. PAUL'S CHURCH, LOOKING EAST,
SOUTH AND WEST, 1849

Drawn by John William Hill
Engraved in aquatint by Henry Papprill
Published by Henry J. Megarey

See Catalogue No. 104.

71. VIEW OF RICHMOND, VA., [1853]

Drawn by John William Hill
Lithographed by Fanny Palmer
Printed in tints by Francis Michelin
Published by Smith Brothers

Typical of the many city views of towns up and down the Atlantic seaboard drawn by Hill for Smith Brothers, this lithograph of Richmond combines the talents of Hill, Fanny Palmer, and Francis Michelin. Michelin was involved in early experiments with color lithography as early as 1840, when he

was associated with the pioneer color lithographer, William Sharp, in Boston (See Frontispiece).

BROOKLYN, L. I. AS SEEN
FROM TRINITY CHURCH, NEW YORK, 1853

Painted by John William Hill
Published by Smith Brothers

See Catalogue No. 96.

72. PORTLAND, ME., 1855

Painted by John William Hill
Lithograph by Charles Parsons
Printed by Endicott & Co.
Published by Smith Brothers

Charles Parsons, who transferred many of John William Hill's views to the lithographic stone for the firm of Smith Brothers, was later to become one of the most prolific artists associated with Currier & Ives. It was while in Portland making sketches for this lithograph that John William Hill discovered a copy of Ruskin's *Modern Painters*, which transformed his idea of the artist's calling, and eventually led to his totally abandoning topographical drawing in favor of pure landscape and still life in a "pre-Raphaelite" style.

PLATE 13   Portland, Me., 1855. Lithograph after John William Hill. [Cat. No. 72]. Graphic Arts Collection. Gift of Leonard L. Milberg '53.

NEW YORK FROM THE STEEPLE OF
ST. PAUL'S CHURCH, LOOKING EAST, SOUTH
AND WEST, 1855

Drawn by John William Hill
Engraved by Henry Papprill
Published by Joseph Laing & Co.

See Catalogue No. 105.

73. BOSTON, 1853

Original watercolor by John William Hill
Signed and dated 1853

John William Hill's large engraved views of New York and Boston were among the last topographical subjects published by the artist, who abandoned the genre for pure landscape in the mid-1850's. Perhaps this magnificent watercolor, somewhat reminiscent of similar harbor scenes by J.M.W. Turner, already reflects Hill's aspirations as a serious landscape painter. It combines the detailed accuracy of the topographical view with an interest in sweeping atmospheric effects unusual in such works, and indeed the distant skyline of Boston seems almost less important than the lively activity of the harbor in the foreground and the dramatic play of light and shade in sea and sky (See Plate 4).

GRAPHIC ARTS COLLECTION
GIFT OF LEONARD L. MILBERG '53

74. BOSTON, 1857

Painted by John William Hill
Engraved by Charles Mottram
Published by Paul & Dominic Colnaghi, London;
Smith Brothers, New York; François Delarue, Paris

Hill's *Boston* was engraved and printed in England. Although the engraving closely reproduces Hill's composition, it varies from it in several details, notably in the introduction of the large sailing ship in the center of the harbor, and in the added emphasis on the two smokestacks on the right horizon, which were barely indicated by Hill. The sky has also been modified to suggest a passing storm, and its handling is somewhat more conventional than in Hill's watercolor. The spectacular results that Hill obtained in his last engravings lead one to regret that he chose to abandon topographical drawing at this point in his career (See Plate 5).

GRAPHIC ARTS COLLECTION
GIFT OF LEONARD L. MILBERG '53

FREDERICK CATHERWOOD (1799-1854)

The English architect and topographical artist Frederick Catherwood is better known for his views of the Near East and of the pre-Columbian ruins of Central America than for American city views. After early travels in Italy, Greece and Egypt, Catherwood came to New York about 1836. In 1839, he made his famous voyage to Central America, and in 1844 published *View of Ancient Monuments in Central America, Chiapas and Yucatan.* He was lost on the steamer *Arctic* in 1854.

75. NEW YORK, TAKEN FROM THE NORTH WEST ANGLE OF FORT COLUMBUS, GOVERNOR'S ISLAND, 1846

Drawn by Frederick Catherwood
Engraved in aquatint by Henry Papprill
Published by Henry J. Megarey

Papprill's aquatint of Catherwood's view of New York from Governor's Island should be compared to the final plate of the *Hudson River Port Folio,* engraved by John Hill from a painting by William Guy Wall more than twenty years earlier.

LEONARD L. MILBERG COLLECTION

FITZ HUGH LANE (1804-1865)

Better known as a painter of luminous seascapes, Fitz Hugh Lane trained as a lithographer in the pioneer Boston firm of William S. Pendleton, and was later employed by the Boston publishers Keith & Moore, for whom he drew several city views. In the 1840's he formed a partnership with John W. A. Scott, another former Pendleton apprentice, and together they issued a number of very beautiful and very scarce lithographic views. Although often degraded into a cheap commercial reproductive technique, lithography emerges as a fine art in its own right in the hands of a talented artist such as Fitz Hugh Lane.

76. THE NATIONAL LANCERS WITH THE REVIEWING OFFICERS ON BOSTON COMMON, 1837

Drawn by Charles Hubbard
Lithographed by Fitz Hugh Lane
Published by Moore's Lithography

This view of Boston Common, with the State House in the background, is a good example of Lane's early reproductive work. Technically competent, it has a slightly primitive character which is probably a reflection of the style of sign painter Charles Hubbard, whose painted military standard served as the model for Lane's lithograph.

LEONARD L. MILBERG COLLECTION

PLATE 14   View of Gloucester, Mass., 1855. Lithograph by Fitz Hugh Lane. [Cat. No. 79]. Graphic Arts Collection.
Gift of Leonard L. Milberg '53.

77. VIEW IN BOSTON HARBOR

Drawn by Fitz Hugh Lane
Published by Moore's Lithography

A festive air pervades this brightly-colored, very rare view of Boston Harbor from the late 1830's, dedicated by its publisher Thomas Moore to the "Tiger Boat Club," whose shell appears in the foreground. Lane's debt to the marine cityscapes of such artists as Birch and Bennett is fully apparent in the somewhat conventional composition, and the lithographer even appears to have tried to imitate the characteristic textures of an aquatint engraving in transferring his drawing to the lithographic stone.

LEONARD L. MILBERG COLLECTION

78. VIEW OF THE BATTLE GROUND AT CONCORD, MASS., c. 1840

Drawn by Fitz Hugh Lane
Published by Thayer's Lithography

Lane provided the drawing that served as the basis for this lovely pastoral landscape with its remarkably informal composition. It is not clear whether he also executed the lithograph. Benjamin W. Thayer bought out Moore's Lithography at 204 Washington Street in Boston in 1840; Moore, an Englishman who had served as William S. Pendleton's bookkeeper, had run the former Pendleton shop since 1835.

LEONARD L. MILBERG COLLECTION

79. VIEW OF GLOUCESTER, MASS., 1855

Painted and lithographed by Fitz Hugh Lane
Published by Procter Brothers

Lane was a native of Gloucester, and had executed a lithograph of the seaport town for Pendleton's as early as 1835. This later lithograph of the same subject is indisputably one of his finest works, evoking the luminous quality typical of his paintings through its low horizons, vast expanse of sky, and motionless sailboats reflected in the calm harbor.

GRAPHIC ARTS COLLECTION
GIFT OF LEONARD L. MILBERG '53

TAPPAN AND BRADFORD

Eben Tappan and Lodowick H. Bradford were active in Boston from the early 1830's through the early 1850's, at the same time that Fitz Hugh Lane was producing his city views. They printed several of the early views by Benjamin Franklin Smith, Jr., and also did printing work for the successful publishing firm of Smith Brothers, established by Smith in 1848. Smith's drawings were among those included in *View in New England*, a series of lithographs printed by Tappan & Bradford in 1849.

80. BOSTON FROM TELEGRAPH HILL

Lithographed by Tappan & Bradford

GRAPHIC ARTS COLLECTION
GIFT OF LEONARD L. MILBERG '53

HENRY WALTON (1804-1865)

The prints of Henry Walton have much of the naive charm of folk art, and there is very little to substantiate the claim that Walton—presumably the son of the wealthy Judge Walton of Saratoga Springs—may have studied in England. Although perspective is generally handled competently in Walton's most typical prints, volumes are simplified, figures are stiff and awkward, and the compositions are organized with an eye for pattern and detail that is not unrelated to the latter day patchwork landscapes of a Grandma Moses.

By 1830, Walton was sketching scenes around Saratoga Springs for John H. Steel's *An Analysis of the Mineral Waters of Ballston . . .* (1831) and *Fashionable Tour: A Guide to Travellers Visiting the Middle and Northern States and the Provinces of Canada* (1830), where they were reproduced as lithographs by Pendleton's of Boston and as engravings by Rawdon, Wright & Co. of New York. By 1836, he was settled in Ithaca; the earliest of his views of that city, *A East View of Ithaca, Tompkins County*, dates from that year. Walton continued to produce views of upstate New York towns until 1851, when he joined a party of gold seekers setting out for California. Only a single view, a watercolor probably intended for reproduction as a lithograph, is known from this California period.

81. A EAST VIEW OF ITHACA, TOMPKINS COUNTY, N.Y. TAKEN IN SEPT. 1836

Drawn from nature and on stone by Henry Walton
Printed by John H. Bufford

The figures in the foreground, quaintly posed like old-fashioned wooden toys, help to make this earliest view of Ithaca one of Walton's most appealing prints.

LENT BY STANLEY KOMAROFF

PLATE 15   View of Ithaca, Tompkins County, N.Y. Taken from the West Hill, 1839. Lithograph by Henry Walton. [Cat. No. 83].
Graphic Arts Collection. Gift of Leonard L. Milberg '53.

82. A View of Ithaca, Tompkins County, N.Y. Taken from the South Hill in November 1838

Drawn from nature and on stone by Henry Walton
Printed by John H. Bufford

The canal building boom of the 1830's is reflected in the caption to this print, which indicates that "Vessels are introduced upon the Lake to shew [sic] the Result of the Sodus Canal being made according to Plan."

LEONARD L. MILBERG COLLECTION

83. View of Ithaca, Tompkins County, N.Y. Taken from the West Hill, 1839

Drawn from nature and on stone by Henry Walton
Printed by Daniel S. Jenkins

Walton appears to have been interested in portraying Ithaca's still rural charm rather than its growth and expansion; this latest view is in many ways the most rustic of the three. Cornell University, today situated in Ithaca, was not founded until 1865.

GRAPHIC ARTS COLLECTION
GIFT OF LEONARD L. MILBERG '53

THOMAS WHELPLEY

A citizen of Cleveland, Thomas Whelpley was responsible for a series of at least four views of that city as it appeared in 1833, full of charming primitive details such as the farmer plowing and the sheep nibbling the bushes in the view from Brooklyn Hill looking east. Like Birch's views of Philadelphia, Whelpley's views are an attempt to provide a comprehensive picture of the city as it appeared at a single point in time, in contrast to the views by some other artists which document their cities' growth and development. Whelpley's views of Cleveland were engraved by Milo Osborne, who was also known for his New York views.

84. Cleveland, Ohio from Brooklyn Hill Looking East, 1834

Drawn by Thomas Whelpley
Engraved by Milo Osborne
Published by Thomas Whelpley

LEONARD L. MILBERG COLLECTION

85. Cleveland, Ohio from the Buffalo Road East of the Court House, 1834

Drawn by Thomas Whelpley
Engraved by Milo Osborne
Published by Thomas Whelpley

LEONARD L. MILBERG COLLECTION

PLATE 16   Cleveland, Ohio from Brooklyn Hill Looking East, 1834. Engraving after Thomas Whelpley. [Cat. No. 84].
Leonard L. Milberg Collection.

86. CLEVELAND, OHIO FROM THE COURT HOUSE LOOKING WEST, 1834

Drawn by Thomas Whelpley
Engraved by Milo Osborne
Published by Thomas Whelpley

LEONARD L. MILBERG COLLECTION

87. CLEVELAND, OHIO FROM THE CORNER OF BANK AND ST. CLAIR STR. LOOKING EAST, 1834

Drawn by Thomas Whelpley
Engraved by Milo Osborne
Published by Thomas Whelpley

LEONARD L. MILBERG COLLECTION

HAVERHILL, MASSACHUSETTS IN 1818

The Morse who engraved this delightful primitive view of Haverhill, on the Merrimac River in northeastern Massachusetts, was probably Hazen Morse, who is listed in the Boston directory from 1818 to 1843. Morse was not primarily active as an engraver of city views, nor indeed of artists' drawings of any kind. Most of his trade was apparently in engraved nameplates for doors and coffin-lids. Another drawing by Mrs. Green of c. 1825-26 was reproduced as a lithograph at a slightly later date.

88. A VIEW OF THE TOWN OF HAVERHILL, MASS., c. 1818

Drawn by Mrs. S. R. Green
Engraved in aquatint by Morse

GRAPHIC ARTS COLLECTION
GIFT OF LEONARD L. MILBERG '53

AMERICA AT MID-CENTURY

As the century moved on, print production became increasingly big business, and the city view was a popular genre that no successful print publisher could afford to ignore. Lithographic printing and publishing firms proliferated and nearly all produced at least some city views. Tappan & Bradford of Boston and Endicott & Co. of New York both printed city views for Smith Brothers, who published so many of the later city views by John William Hill. Endicott & Co. also did a great deal of printing for the most famous of all nineteenth-century print publishers, Currier & Ives. Like many early American lithographers, Nathaniel Currier (1813-1888) was trained as an apprentice by William S. Pendleton. In 1857 he formed the partnership with James Merritt Ives (1824-1895), whose business acumen was probably responsible for the firm's great commercial success. Currier & Ives are not usually thought of as publishers of American views, but in fact they issued a large number of straightforward city views, as well as imaginary scenes and genre subjects in actual urban or rural settings which contribute to our vision of America in the mid-nineteenth century.

89. SAINT PAUL. CAPITAL OF MINNESOTA, MAY 1856

Painted by S. H. Andrews
Lithographed by Endicott & Co.
Published by Hamilton & Co.

St. Paul had been incorporated as the capital of the new territory of Minnesota as recently as 1849. A pride in western expansion is characteristic of American views at mid-century, with the new western towns and frontier settlements frequently appearing as subjects.

GRAPHIC ARTS COLLECTION
GIFT OF LEONARD L. MILBERG '53

90. PROVIDENCE, R.I. VIEW FROM WEST BANK OF THE RIVER

Drawn and lithographed by J. P. Newell
Printed at John H. Bufford's

Artists also found new ways of looking at familiar eastern subjects and the romantic, pastoral quality of earlier topographical views was replaced by a greater realism, emphasizing burgeoning commerce and industry, unashamed of such earthy details as warehouses, coal and lumberyards, and smokestacks billowing forth great clouds of black smoke. J. P. Newell's view of Providence, Rhode Island, dating from c. 1858-60, should be compared to Edwin Whitefield's slightly earlier and dramatically different view of the same city.

GRAPHIC ARTS COLLECTION
GIFT OF LEONARD L. MILBERG '53

91. MIDDLETOWN, CONN.

Drawn from nature by Ferdinand Mayer
Printed by John D. Dumcke and Valentine Keil
Published by S. N. Gaston

By mid-century, lithographed views of the smaller towns of America were beginning to appear in much greater numbers than ever before, as travelling artists sought for commissions from their citizens, often enlisting local merchants as publishers. The lithographers Dumcke & Keil were active in New York c. 1855-57, so this print of Middletown, Connecticut after a drawing by Ferdinand Mayer must date from this period.

GRAPHIC ARTS COLLECTION
GIFT OF LEONARD L. MILBERG '53

EDWIN WHITEFIELD (1816-1892)

Edwin Whitefield is a good example of a typical nineteenth-century phenomenon: the itinerant artist. Like the itinerant portrait painter, who made his way from place to place in search of commissions for portraits, the itinerant topographical draughtsman travelled about the country sketching cities and soliciting subscriptions from their citizens for the finished prints, which were executed only if sufficient interest was aroused. *Whitefield's Views of American Cities*, issued from c. 1845-c. 1856, included at least thirty-seven large folio views and numerous smaller ones, for which Whitefield was both artist and publisher. Sometimes he even transferred his drawings to the lithographic stone himself, but in most cases he left this aspect of the procedure, as well as the actual printing, to others, often to Francis Michelin, who also printed so many city views for Smith Brothers.

92. VIEW OF BROOKLYN, L.I., FROM U.S. HOTEL, NEW YORK, 1846

Drawn from nature and on stone by Edwin Whitefield
Printed by Francis Michelin
Published by Edwin Whitefield

This view of Brooklyn, "drawn from nature and on stone by Edwin Whitefield," is one of the earliest and most attractive of *Whitefield's Views of American Cities*. Whitefield's composition seems to have been directly influenced by Bennett's engraving of John William Hill's vista of New York from Brooklyn (1836), which represents the same stretch of the East River seen from the opposite shore, and from a similar elevated viewpoint.

LEONARD L. MILBERG COLLECTION

PLATE 17 View of Providence, R.I. from the North, 1849. Lithograph after Edwin Whitefield. [Cat. No. 93]. Graphic Arts Collection.
Gift of Leonard L. Milberg '53.

93. VIEW OF PROVIDENCE, R.I., FROM THE NORTH, 1849

Drawn by Edwin Whitefield
Drawn on stone by Charles W. Burton
Printed by Francis Michelin
Published by Edwin Whitefield

This later view of Providence, Rhode Island, evidently turned out to be something of a surprise best seller when it was issued in 1849. Whitefield received orders for at least 1,300 copies, "a much larger number than . . . anticipated for such a place as Providence," he noted in his diary. Whitefield's views normally sold for $2.00-$5.00, with higher prices charged for the large, colored versions of the prints.

GRAPHIC ARTS COLLECTION
GIFT OF LEONARD L. MILBERG '53

94. THE HOMES OF OUR FOREFATHERS, BOSTON, 1882

By Edwin Whitefield
Illustrated with lithographs from drawings by Edwin Whitefield

Late in life, Whitefield illustrated several books documenting the colonial architecture of New England. The self-conscious antiquarian focus of this project suggests that Whitefield's earlier *Views of American Cities* was not simply a commercial venture, but was also partly motivated by a real desire, similar to that of John Warner Barber, to record the appearance of the America of his day, so rapidly changing and evolving.

PRINCETON UNIVERSITY LIBRARY
ELIZABETH FOUNDATION

95. NEW YORK AND BROOKLYN WITH JERSEY CITY AND HOBOKEN WATERFRONT, 1877

Drawn and lithographed by Charles R. Parsons and Lyman W. Atwater
Published by Currier & Ives

Charles R. Parsons, the son of Charles Parsons, who sometimes lithographed drawings by John William Hill for Smith Brothers in the 1850's, formed a partnership with Lyman W. Atwater in 1863. Like his father, the younger Parsons drew and lithographed landscape and marine views for the well-known firm of Currier & Ives. The characteristic city views of Parsons & Atwater employ bird's-eye perspective, continuing the tradition established earlier in the century by such artists as Bachman and Sachse.

LEONARD L. MILBERG COLLECTION

SMITH BROTHERS

The four Smith Brothers, Benjamin Franklin, Jr., George Warren, Francis and David Clifford Smith, were in the print publishing business from 1848 to 1857. It was they who commissioned John William Hill's vast series of American city views in the early 1850's, including his views of Richmond, Virginia (Cat. No. 71), Portland, Maine (Cat. No. 72) and Brooklyn, New York (Cat. No. 96). One of the brothers, Benjamin Franklin Smith, Jr. (1830-1927), was himself a talented draughtsman, most of whose topographical work conforms to the same general format as the later lithographs after Hill and Whitefield, consisting of distant views of cities, often seen from across a river or other body of water, with pastoral elements in the foreground and a low horizon line. After 1857, Smith abandoned his career as an artist. He went into banking, and when he died in 1927 he was one of the richest men in New England.

96. BROOKLYN, L.I., AS SEEN FROM TRINITY CHURCH, NEW YORK, 1853

Painted by John William Hill
Published by Smith Brothers

Another of the numerous city views drawn by John William Hill for Smith Brothers.

LEONARD L. MILBERG COLLECTION

97. NEW HAVEN, CONN. FROM FERRY HILL, 1848

Drawn by Benjamin Franklin Smith, Jr.
Lithographed by Tappan & Bradford
Published by D. C. & B. F. Smith, Jr.

This view of New Haven, Connecticut, from a drawing by Benjamin Franklin Smith, Jr., is virtually indistinguishable in style and conception from the many lithographs after John William Hill, also published by Smith Brothers.

GRAPHIC ARTS COLLECTION
GIFT OF LEONARD L. MILBERG '53

98. BROOKLYN, N.Y., 1854

Drawn by Benjamin Franklin Smith, Jr.
Engraved by Wellstood & Peters
Published by A. Merwin

Some of Benjamin Franklin Smith, Jr.'s most spectacular works, such as his view of *New York from the Latting Observatory* and this view of *Brooklyn* from 1854, were engraved in copper by William Wellstood and printed by Henry Peters.

LEONARD L. MILBERG COLLECTION

OPTICAL AIDS

Photography was first invented in 1839, and city views were among the earliest photographic subjects. Even before the invention of photography, topographical artists often used optical devices, such as the camera lucida, which employed a prism and mirror to reflect an image of a scene on a sheet of paper, which might then be traced to produce a precise rendering, exact in every detail. The new art of photography was considered a similar optical aid, and photographs were consulted by artists as supplements to their own sketches. Edward Sachse, a Baltimore lithographer, acknowledged the use of photographic sources for some of his city views, and the "out of focus" rivers in the lithographs of Smith Brothers and some other mid-century firms may indicate that they also consulted contemporary photographs, where such an effect is common, produced by the long exposures that were necessary at the time.

99. VIEW OF ALBANY, CAPITOL OF THE EMPIRE STATE, FROM THE HILLS EAST SIDE THE HUDSON, 1852

Lithographed by Eliphalet M. Brown, Jr.
Printed by A. Robertson
*Published by C. C. Schoonmaker from Daguerreotypes
at his Galleries*

The use of photographic sources is well documented for this 1852 view of Albany, New York. Not only does the inscription state that the composition was taken from daguerreotypes at C. C. Schoonmaker's New York gallery, but the artist even included a photographer and his assistants in the right foreground. This detail may possibly include a self-portrait, since

lithographer Eliphalet M. Brown, Jr. was also a daguerreotypist, and accompanied Commodore Perry's expedition to Japan in this capacity in 1852-54 (See Plate 6).

GRAPHIC ARTS COLLECTION
GIFT OF LEONARD L. MILBERG '53

JOHN WARNER BARBER (1798-1885)

John Warner Barber was a curious combination of topographical draughtsman, engraver and historian, who devoted many years to compiling his *Historical Collections*, a series of books which provides an exhaustive record of the appearance of towns and villages throughout the eastern United States in the early part of the nineteenth century. Barber contributed both text and illustrations, travelling extensively to collect information and make drawings. Unlike most of the works of art in this exhibition, which were printed from heavy metal plates or unwieldy lithographic stones, Barber's illustrations were in the form of wood engravings, printed from small wooden blocks. The technique was related to that used at an earlier date for making woodcuts, but the design was cut on the endgrain of the wood, allowing for relatively fine detail. The blocks could easily be combined with printing type so that wood engraving was much used for the illustration of books and periodicals during the nineteenth century.

100. CENTRAL VIEW IN HIGHTSTOWN, N.J.

Original woodblock by John Warner Barber

GRAPHIC ARTS, SINCLAIR HAMILTON COLLECTION

101. CHARLESTOWN IN JEFFERSON COUNTY, VA.

Original woodblock by John Warner Barber

These actual woodblocks, engraved by John Warner Barber, were used for printing illustrations in *Historical Collections of New Jersey* and *Historical Collections of Virginia*.

GRAPHIC ARTS, SINCLAIR HAMILTON COLLECTION

102. HISTORICAL COLLECTIONS OF THE STATE OF NEW JERSEY, Newark, New Jersey, 1844

By John Warner Barber and Henry Howe
Illustrated by John Warner Barber

DEPARTMENT OF RARE BOOKS
GIFT OF RUNKLE F. HEGEMAN '06

103. EASTERN VIEW OF THE PUBLIC SQUARE OR GREEN, IN NEW HAVEN, CONN., 1840

Drawn and engraved by John Warner Barber
Sold by E. L. and J. W. Barber

In his *Eastern View of the Public Square* in New Haven, Barber has preserved the appearance of the American city that he knew best. He lived and worked in New Haven from 1823 to 1885. Later states of this print record the growth of the elm trees in the foreground.

GRAPHIC ARTS COLLECTION
GIFT OF LEONARD L. MILBERG '53

EXPANDING HORIZONS

The bird's-eye view, depicting the city as if seen from a point high overhead, belongs to a venerable tradition. Bird's-eye views of cities appeared in early atlases, such as Georg Braun's *Civitas Orbis Terrarum* (1575). It is tempting to link the revival of interest in the world as seen from above in the eighteenth and early nineteenth centuries with the first aeronautical experiments. Some European views do exist that are presented "as if" taken from a balloon, but there is no evidence that this device was ever employed by American artists. City views using an extremely elevated viewpoint began to appear around 1850; John William Hill's 1849 panorama of *New York from the Steeple of St. Paul's Church* is an early example. Slightly later artists such as Edward Sachse and John Bachman adopted even higher, purely imaginary viewpoints. Such viewpoints made it possible to include larger and larger expanses of rapidly expanding cities such as New York, to portray the entire city instead of one selected vista. Extreme examples of the bird's-eye view are virtually three-dimensional maps, and some of them, such as the *View of Los Angeles from the East* (Cat. No. 117), even include the names of streets and other landmarks.

104. New York from the Steeple of St. Paul's Church, Looking East, South and West, 1849

Drawn by John William Hill
Engraved in aquatint by Henry Papprill
Published by Henry J. Megarey

The Indian summer of aquatint engraving in America is represented by this spectacular view of the corner of Broadway and Fulton Street in New York, drawn by John William Hill and engraved by Henry Papprill. Hill's viewpoint on the steeple of St. Paul's Church permitted him to present not only one of the earliest bird's-eye views of the city, but also to convey a lively sense of the bustling activity of the street, which he does with a keen notation of realistic detail. Brady's Daguerrian Gallery and Barnum's Museum figure prominently in the foreground.

LEONARD L. MILBERG COLLECTION

105. New York from the Steeple of St. Paul's Church, Looking East, South and West, 1855

Drawn by John William Hill
Engraved in aquatint by Henry Papprill
Published by Joseph Laing & Co.

Brady's Daguerrian Gallery and Barnum's Museum still occupy the same positions in this later state of the Hill-Papprill view, but the names have been changed on many other buildings and stories have been added to some of them, reflecting the rapidly changing appearance of the city between 1849 and 1855.

GRAPHIC ARTS COLLECTION
GIFT OF LEONARD L. MILBERG '53

PLATE 18   New York from the Steeple of St. Paul's Church, Looking East, South and West, 1849. Aquatint after John William Hill. [Cat. No. 104]. Leonard L. Milberg Collection.

PLATE 19   Detail of New York from the Steeple of St. Paul's
Church, Looking East, South and West, 1855. Aquatint after John
William Hill. [Cat. No. 105]. Graphic Arts Collection.
Gift of Leonard L. Milberg '53.

EDWARD SACHSE (1804-1873)

Edward Sachse came to the United States from Germany in the 1840's and with his brother Theodore opened a lithographic printing establishment in Baltimore, Maryland. Most of their output consisted of brightly colored bird's-eye views of cities in Maryland, Virginia, West Virginia and the District of Columbia; they also issued some important contemporary Civil War subjects of considerable topographical interest, such as *The Naval Engagement Between the Merrimac and the Monitor at Hampton Roads* and *The Siege of Yorktown, April, 1862.*

106. BIRD'S-EYE VIEW OF THE CITY OF ANNAPOLIS, CAPITAL OF THE STATE OF MARYLAND

Lithographed by Edward Sachse & Co.
Published by Edward Sachse & Co.

This bird's-eye view of Annapolis, dating from the 1850's, is a good example of the work of Sachse & Co. An "updated" version of the print was published in a reduced format by Charles Magnus in 1864. Like the two states of the Hill-Papprill view of New York, these two versions of the same view of Annapolis document the growth of that city in the intervening years.

GRAPHIC ARTS COLLECTION
GIFT OF LEONARD L. MILBERG '53

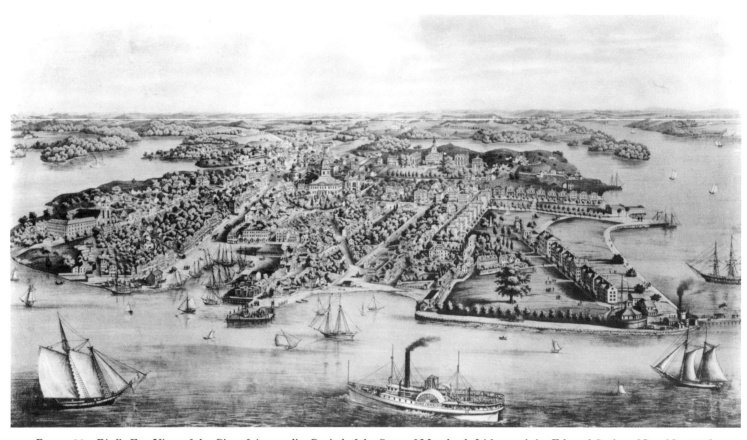

PLATE 20   Bird's-Eye View of the City of Annapolis, Capital of the State of Maryland. Lithograph by Edward Sachse. [Cat. No. 106].
Graphic Arts Collection. Gift of Leonard L. Milberg '53.

107. VIEW OF INDIANAPOLIS, C. 1854

Drawn from nature and printed in colors
by Edward Sachse & Co.
Published by J. T. Palmatary

GRAPHIC ARTS COLLECTION
GIFT OF LEONARD L. MILBERG '53

108. VIEW OF GEORGETOWN, D.C.

Lithographed and printed in colors by Edward Sachse & Co.
Published by Edward Sachse & Co.

GRAPHIC ARTS COLLECTION
GIFT OF LEONARD L. MILBERG '53

JOHN BACHMAN (fl. 1849-1877)

John Bachman, or Bachmann, as he also spelled his name at times, specialized in bird's-eye views, especially of New York, taken from extremely elevated viewpoints high above the city, and he achieved effects that were to remain unequaled until the advent of aerial photography. C. Bachmann, who drew a similar bird's-eye view of New York in 1849 (Cat. No. 109), was probably a relative. One state of C. Bachmann's print lists John Bachmann as the publisher.

109. NEW YORK, 1849

Drawn from nature and on stone by C. Bachmann
Printed by Sarony & Major
Published by Williams & Stevens

This bird's-eye view of New York belongs to a type that would become increasingly popular as the century progressed. While the J. W. Hill panoramas employed rooftop or steeple-top vantage points, Bachmann's purely imaginary viewpoint is situated in midair, high above Union Square.

LEONARD L. MILBERG COLLECTION

110. BIRD'S EYE VIEW OF NEW YORK AND BROOKLYN, 1850

Drawn from nature and on stone by John Bachman
Printed by John Bachman
Published by John Bachman

While the panoramas of earlier artist, and especially those of John W. Hill, retained a human scale and at best even succeeded in capturing something of the street life of the early cities as well as their physical topography, the extremely elevated viewpoints of these later bird's-eye views produces an effect that is much more impersonal.

111. BIRD'S-EYE VIEW OF NEW ORLEANS, 1851

Drawn on stone by John Bachman
Printed by John Bachman
Published by the Agents A. Guerber & Co.

The extraordinary and highly accurate detail of Bachman's prints and the crystal clarity of his vision are well-represented in this view of New Orleans published in 1851. Bachman's achievement appears even more extraordinary when one considers that this elaborate bird's-eye view was composed entirely from studies made at ground level, which were then reconstructed in perspective to meet the requirements of his imaginary aerial viewpoint.

112. VIEW OF CENTRAL PARK, NEW YORK

Drawn by John Bachmann [sic]
Printed by H. Bencke

In many ways more charming than his overall views of entire cities are those prints in which Bachman concentrated on a smaller area, as in this sunny, pastoral vision of New York's Central Park in its pristine condition. While early artists were able to relate the American city to the countryside by situating it in its unspoiled landscape setting, Olmstead's Central Park attempted to re-create an artificial romantic landscape playground in the midst of the city itself.

PLATE 21   Bird's-Eye View of New Orleans, 1851. Lithograph by John Bachman. [Cat. No. 111]. Graphic Arts Collection.
Gift of Leonard L. Milberg '53.

PLATE 22   San-Francisco, 1849. Lithograph after Henry Firks. [Cat. No. 113]. Leonard L. Milberg Collection.

WESTERN CITY VIEWS

The discovery of gold at Sutter's Mill in Coloma, California in 1848 resulted in a wild stampede of treasure-seeking adventurers from all parts of the world, and incidentally produced a minor "school" of lithography, differing in many ways from typical Eastern prints. Mostly uncolored, produced in small runs and on cheap paper, the earliest California views sold for a few cents apiece, and were frequently folded and mailed home by forty-niners to give family and friends some notion of the appearance of the boom towns and mining camps. Eastern firms such as Currier & Ives also responded to the demand for accurate views of the gold fields.

113. San-Francisco, 1849

Drawn on the spot by Henry Firks for W. H. Jones, Esq.
Drawn on stone by Arvah J. Ibbotson
Printed by Thomas Sinclair

Thomas Sinclair, a Philadelphia lithographer, scooped his competitors to publish this first view of San Francisco after the discovery of gold, relying upon a drawing mailed east by a California merchant.

LEONARD L. MILBERG COLLECTION

KUCHEL AND DRESEL

The San Francisco firm of Charles C. Kuchel and Emil Dresel issued a series of "Pacific Views," somewhat on the idea of "Whitefield's Views of American Cities," in 1855-58, travelling about to obtain subscribers and often enlisting local publishers for their prints. The series includes most of the major cities and mining towns of California, Oregon and Washington, and provides important documentation for this fascinating period of history.

114. Coloma, 1857

Drawn and lithographed by Kuchel & Dresel
Printed by Britton & Rey
Published by George Searle

Typical of Kuchel & Dresel's views, with its central panorama surrounded by vignettes showing local businesses, this lithograph of Coloma, California, represents the site where gold was first discovered in 1848.

LEONARD L. MILBERG COLLECTION

115. Scotts Bar and French Bar, 1856

Drawn from nature and on stone by Kuchel & Dresel
Printed by Britton and Rey
Published by J.M.C. Jones

Almost no mining town was too small to attract the attention of Kuchel and Dresel, and even small mining camps such as Scotts Bar and French Bar were apparently able to produce enough subscribers to make this rare lithograph a profitable venture.

116. Los Angeles, Los Angeles County, Cal., 1857

Drawn from nature and on stone by Kuchel & Dresel
Printed by Britton & Rey

This rare, early state of Kuchel & Dresel's *Los Angeles* shows the humble beginnings of the sprawling twentieth-century metropolis.

117. View of Los Angeles from the East

Drawn by E. S. Glover
Lithographed by A. L. Bancroft & Co.
Published by the Brooklyn Land and Building Co.

This view of Los Angeles from the East shows a flourishing Victorian town in contrast to the primitive adobe settlement depicted almost exactly twenty years earlier by Kuchel & Dresel. It was probably issued as part of a land development scheme, conforming to a common practice, by the Brooklyn Land and Building Co., who were presumably the proprietors of the new lots in the foreground.

118. View of Honolulu from the Catholic Church, c. 1854

Drawn by Paul Emmert
Printed by Britton & Rey

Paul Emmert, a New York lithographer, was apparently one of those artists drawn to the West by the California Gold Rush of 1849, for his name appears on "Emmert and Penfield's Original Panorama of the Gold Mines," shown in New York in 1850-51. This view of Honolulu, "drawn from Nature," and published in San Francisco in 1854, documents his travels even farther afield. In style and format it closely resembles the work of Kuchel and Dresel, which was also reproduced by Britton & Rey.

PLATE 23   Los Angeles, Los Angeles County, Cal., 1857. Lithograph by Charles C. Kuchel and Emil Dresel. [Cat. No. 116].
Graphic Arts Collection. Gift of Leonard L. Milberg '53.

HENRY LEWIS (1819-1904)

The seventy-eight plates of Henry Lewis's *Das Illustrierte Mississippithal* of 1854, depicting scenes between the Falls of St. Anthony in Minnesota and the Gulf of Mexico, document the frontier settlements and wild scenery of the Mississippi River Valley in a format derived from earlier publications on the Hudson River Valley. Lewis, who was born on the English-Welsh border in 1819, settled in St. Louis in 1836. He spent the summers of 1846 and 1847 floating down the Mississippi making sketches for a mile-long panorama which he completed in 1849. He exhibited this panorama in Europe in 1850 and settled in Düsseldorf, where *Das Illustrierte Mississippithal*, with color lithographs based on Lewis's sketches, was published in 1854.

119. CAIRO, MOUTH OF THE OHIO— ARTIST'S ENCAMPMENT—BURLINGTON, IOWA—SAVANNAH, ILLINOIS—CASSVILLE IN 1829—BELLEVUE, IOWA—PRAIRIE DU CHIEN, WISCONSIN IN 1830

Painted by Henry Lewis
Lithographed by Arnz & Co., Düsseldorf

It was not the vast expanses of river and prairie that fascinated Lewis as much as the thriving settlements, rapidly growing towns and bustling commerce along the river banks. *Artist's Encampment* depicts Lewis's own party camped on one of the many little islands along the course of the Mississippi.

GRAPHIC ARTS COLLECTION
GIFT OF LEONARD L. MILBERG '53

120. DAS ILLUSTRIERTE MISSISSIPPITHAL, Düsseldorf, 1854

Illustrated by Henry Lewis

COLLECTIONS OF WESTERN AMERICANA
PRINCETON UNIVERSITY LIBRARY

ALFRED E. MATHEWS (1831-1874)

After serving with the Union forces during the Civil War and producing numerous battle sketches, Alfred E. Mathews moved to Denver, Colorado, where he concentrated on the western scene, mingling views of frontier towns with sublime landscapes on an infinitely vaster scale than anything to be seen in the East. Many of these drawings were sent by Mathews to New York, where they were reproduced as lithographs by Julius Bien. Best known for his chromolithographic reproductions of Audubon's *Birds of America* (1860; not to be confused with the superb Havell aquatints of the original double elephant folio of 1827-38), Bien is not usually thought of as a lithographer of city views. Actually he was responsible for quite a few, including the Mathews western scenes and an 1866 panorama of New York after John Bachman. Mathews produced in all three books of western scenery: *Pencil Sketches of Colorado* (1866), *Pencil Sketches of Montana* (1868), and *Gems of Western Scenery* (1869).

121. F STREET, DENVER, COLORADO, 1866

Drawn by Alfred E. Mathews
Lithographed by Julius Bien

By entitling his book *Pencil Sketches of Colorado*, Mathews emphasized the ability of the lithographic medium to reproduce exactly the quality of a pencil drawing, an ability little appreciated by most earlier American lithographers, who often seem to have tried to imitate the effects of aquatint. The apparently hasty and careless character of Mathew's "pencil sketches" ideally translates the "rough and ready" character of the frontier towns that were his subjects.

GRAPHIC ARTS COLLECTION
GIFT OF LEONARD L. MILBERG '53

122. BLAKE STREET, DENVER, COLORADO, 1866

Drawn by Alfred E. Mathews
Lithographed by Julius Bien

A similar vitality pervades this second "sketch" of Denver, with its wooden sidewalks thronging with sauntering cowboys and gamblers, its muddy streets full of pigs, dogs, cows, mules and horses.

GRAPHIC ARTS COLLECTION
GIFT OF LEONARD L. MILBERG '53

123. PENCIL SKETCHES OF MONTANA, NEW YORK, 1868

Illustrations by Alfred E. Mathews

PHILIP ASHTON ROLLINS COLLECTION OF WESTERN AMERICANA, PRINCETON UNIVERSITY LIBRARY

124. GEMS OF ROCKY MOUNTAIN SCENERY, NEW YORK, 1869

Illustrations by Alfred E. Mathews

PHILIP ASHTON ROLLINS COLLECTION OF WESTERN AMERICANA, PRINCETON UNIVERSITY LIBRARY

AUGUSTUS KOLLNER (1813-1906)

Like a number of mid-century American lithographers, Augustus Kollner emigrated from Germany. He came to Washington in 1839, and by 1840 was settled in Philadelphia, producing military prints for Huddy & Duval and illustrating chapbooks for the American Sunday School Union. He also designed tradecards, labels and invitations for a variety of Philadelphia printers. In the summer, he travelled widely throughout Pennsylvania, New Jersey and New York, south to Delaware, Maryland and Virginia, and west as far as Ohio, making more than five hundred sketches of cities and scenery. In 1848-51, fifty-four of these drawings were published as lithographs by Goupil, Vibert & Company of New York and Paris. Late in life, Kollner frequently elaborated these early drawings into highly finished watercolors and occasional oil paintings, while continuing to make sketches of the Philadelphia area and nearby sights in Southeastern Pennsylvania and New Jersey.

125. RESIDENCE OF WASHINGTON, 1848

Drawn by Augustus Kollner
Lithographed by Deroy
Published by Goupil, Vibert & Cie

THE NEW YORK PUBLIC LIBRARY
ASTOR, LENOX AND TILDEN FOUNDATION

126. CAPITOL, EAST VIEW, 1848

Drawn by Augustus Kollner
Lithographed by Deroy
Published by Goupil, Vibert & Cie

This pair of lithographs from Kollner's *Views of American Cities* is fairly typical of Kollner's early commercial work: rather uninspired though competent renderings of noteworthly architectural monuments and standard picturesque views, such as the inevitable Niagara Falls, for example. There is little to suggest the personal style and charm of his later watercolors.

THE NEW YORK PUBLIC LIBRARY
ASTOR, LENOX AND TILDEN FOUNDATION

127. SCENE ON THE DELAWARE

Watercolor by Augustus Kollner

Although unsigned and undated, this watercolor of a scene along the Delaware River may safely be attributed to Kollner on the basis of its style. In it Kollner reveals his fascination with modern transportation, juxtaposing the mule barge on the canal with the steam engine which would eventually render such canalboats obsolete. The dates of Kollner drawings are difficult to establish, since he continued to make paintings and watercolors from early sketches throughout his life; but considering the primitive model of steam engine represented by the artist, it seems likely that the prototype of this composition was an early work.

GRAPHIC ARTS COLLECTION

128. HIGH FALL NEAR LUMBERVILLE, PA. WEST PART, 1878

Watercolor by Augustus Kollner

Kollner's later watercolors of dense woodland foliage and jumbled rock formations often possess an almost abstract quality which makes them especially attractive to the modern viewer.

LEONARD L. MILBERG COLLECTION

129. THE CRADLE AT MOUNT ROSE, N.J. 3 MILES WEST OF PRINCETON, 1878

Watercolor by Augustus Kollner

Signed and dated September 1, 1878, this watercolor probably dates from the same sketching expedition as the preceding one, which is dated August 23 of the same year.

GRAPHIC ARTS COLLECTION
GIFT OF LEONARD L. MILBERG '53

130. RAVINE IN N.J. ABOVE PT. PLEASANT, PA., 1886

Watercolor by Augustus Kollner

GRAPHIC ARTS COLLECTION
GIFT OF LEONARD L. MILBERG '53

SELECTED BIBLIOGRAPHY

Baigell, Matthew, *19th-Century Painters of the Delaware Valley*, Trenton, New Jersey State Museum, 1983.

Birch, William Russell, "Autobiography," Unpublished manuscript, Historical Society of Philadelphia.

Comstock, Helen, "The Complete Work of Robert Havell, Jr.," *Connoisseur*, Vol. CXXVI (1950), p. 127.

Comstock, Helen, "Kollner's Views of American Cities," *Old Print Shop Portfolio* 3 (May 1944), pp. 195-203.

Comstock, Helen, "The Rediscovery of George Harvey," *Connoisseur*, Vol. CXXII (1948), pp. 120-121.

Comstock, Helen, "Watercolors in the Hudson River Portfolio," *Connoisseur*, Vol. CXX (1947), pp. 42-43.

Cowdrey, Mary Bartlett, "William Henry Bartlett and the American Scene," *New York History* (1941), pp. 388-400.

Deak, Gloria Gilda, *American Views, Prospects and Vistas*, New York, New York Public Library, 1976.

Diebold, William, "Bartlett's Hudson River Prints," *Imprint* 3 (April 1978), pp. 8-11, 15.

Fielding, Mantle, *American Engravers upon Copper and Steel*, Philadelphia, 1917.

Force, Albert W., "H. Walton-Limner, Lithographer and Map Maker," *Antiques* (September 1962), pp. 284-285.

Groce, George C. and David H. Wallace, *The New York Historical Society's Dictionary of Artists in America 1564-1860*, New Haven and London, 1957.

Hamilton, Sinclair, *Early American Book Illustrators and Wood Engravers, 1670-1870*, 2 volumes, Princeton, 1968.

Havell, Harry P., "Robert Havell's 'View of the Hudson from Tarrytown Heights,' " *New York Historical Society Quarterly*, Vol. XXXI (July 1947), pp. 160-162.

Heilbron, Bertha L., "Edwin Whitefield's Minnesota Lakes," *Minnesota History*, Vol. XXXIII (Summer 1953), pp. 247-251.

Hill, John Henry, *John William Hill, An Artist's Memorial*, New York, 1888.

Koke, Richard J., *American Landscape and Genre Painting in the New York Historical Society*, 3 volumes, New York and Boston, 1982.

Koke, Richard J., *A Checklist of the American Engravings of John Hill (1770-1850)*, 1961.

Koke, Richard J., "John Hill, Master of Aquatint 1770-1850," *The New York Historical Society Quarterly*, Vol. XLIII (1959), pp. 51-117.

Mann, Maybelle, "American Landscape Prints," *Art and Antiques*, Vol. IV (1981), pp. 90-99.

McCormick, Gene E., "Fitz Hugh Lane, Gloucester Artist (1804-1865)," *Art Quarterly*, Vol. XV (Winter 1952), pp. 291-306.

Mumey, Nolie, *Alfred Edward Mathews 1831-1874, Union Soldier, Illustrator of Civil War Battles, Author, Traveler, Map Maker and Delineator of Western Scenes Especially Those of the Territories of Colorado and Montana*, Boulder, Colo., 1961.

Nash, Chauncey C., "John Warner Barber and his Books," *Walpole Society Note Book* (1934), pp. 30-60.

Norton, Bettina A., "Edwin Whitefield 1816-1892," *Antiques*, Vol. CII (August 1972), pp. 232-243.

Norton, Bettina A., *Edwin Whitefield-Nineteenth Century North American Scenery*, Barre, Mass., 1977.

Parker, Barbara Neville, "George Harvey and his Atmospheric Landscapes," *Bulletin of the Museum of Fine Arts* (Boston), Vol. XL (February 1943), pp. 7-9.

Patterson, Margaret Sloane, "Nicolino Calyo and his Paintings of the Great Fire of New York, December 16th & 17th 1835," *The American Art Journal*, Vol. XIV (Spring 1982), pp. 4-22.

Pattison, Robert, "Robert Havell, Junior," *Quarterly Bulletin* (Westchester County Historical Society), Vol. 12 (January 1936), pp. 12-17.

Peters, Harry T., *America on Stone*, New York, 1931.

Peters, Harry T., *California on Stone*, Garden City, N.Y., 1935.

Pleasants, J. Hall, "George Beck, an Early Baltimore Landscape Painter," *Maryland Historical Magazine*, Vol. XXXV (1940), pp. 241-243.

Rehner, Leigh, *Henry Walton: 19th Century American Artist*, Ithaca, New York, Ithaca College Museum of Art, 1968.

Reps, John W., *Cities on Stone: Nineteenth Century Lithograph Images of the Urban West*, Fort Worth, Amon Carter Museum, 1976.

Reps, John W., *Western City Views*, Fort Worth, 1972.

Rowe, L. E., "William Guy Wall," *Antiques*, Vol. IV (1923), pp. 18-22.

Roylance, Dale R., "The Early Prints of New Haven," *New Haven: A Portfolio for the Bicentennial*, New Haven, 1976.

Scott, John, "The Hill Family of Clarksville," *South of the Mountains* (Historical Society of Rockland County), Vol. 19 (1975).

Shelley, Donald A., "George Harvey and His Atmospheric Landscapes of North America," *New York Historical Society Quarterly*, Vol. XXXI (April 1948), pp. 104-113.

Shelley, Donald A., "George Harvey, English Painter of Atmospheric Landscapes in America," *American Collector*, Vol. XVII (April 1948), pp. 10-13.

Shelley, Donald A., "William Guy Wall and his Watercolors for the Historic Hudson River Portfolio," *New York Historical Society Quarterly*, Vol. XXXI (January 1947), pp. 25-45.

Sherman, Constance D., "A French Explorer [Jacques-Gérard Milbert] in the Hudson River Valley," *New York Historical Society Quarterly*, Vol. XLV (July 1961), pp. 255-280.

Snyder, Martin P., "Birch's Philadelphia Views: New Discoveries," *The Pennsylvania Magazine of History and Biography*, Vol. LXXXVIII (1964), pp. 164-173.

Snyder, Martin P., *City of Independence: Views of Philadelphia before 1800*, New York, 1975.

Snyder, Martin P., "William Birch: His Philadelphia Views," *The Pennsylvania Magazine of History and Biography*, Vol. LXXIII (1949), pp. 271-315.

Stauffer, David McNeely, *American Engravers upon Copper and Steel*, 2 volumes, New York, Grolier Club, 1907.

Stokes, I. N. Phelps and Daniel C. Haskell, *American Historical Prints Early Views of American Cities, etc., from the Phelps Stokes and Other Collections*, New York, New York Public Library, 1933.

Stokes, I. N. Phelps, *Iconography of Manhattan Island 1498-1909*, 6 volumes, New York, 1915-1928.

Teitelman, S. Robert, *Birch's Views of Philadelphia: A Reduced Facsimile of The City of Philadelphia . . . as it appeared in the year 1800, with Photographs of the Sites in 1960 and 1982 by S. Robert Teitelman*, Philadelphia, The Free Library, 1982.

Wainwright, Nicholas Biddle, "Augustus Kollner, Artist," *The Pennsylvania Magazine of History and Biography*, Vol. LXXXIV (July 1960), pp. 325-351.

Wainwright, Nicholas Biddle, *Philadelphia in the Romantic Age of Lithography*, Philadelphia, 1958.

Weitenkampf, Frank, "John Hill and American Landscapes in Aquatint," *American Collector*, Vol. XVII (July 1948), pp. 6-8.

Whitefield, Edwin, Diary. Boston Public Library, Print Department. Scrapbook, Boston Public Library, Print Department.

Williams, George A., "Robert Havell, Junior, Engraver of Audubon's 'The Birds of America,'" *Print Collector's Quarterly*, Vol. VI (October 1916), pp. 226-257.

Wilmerding, John, *Fitz Hugh Lane*, 1971.

Wilmerding, John, *Fitz Hugh Lane 1804-1865: American Marine Painter*, Gloucester, Mass., 1967.